A BOOK

A BOOK

with illustrations by

DJUNA BARNES

and an introduction by Torin McLachlan

Reprint of the first edition published by

BONI AND LIVERIGHT, NEW YORK, 1923

ATOPON BOOKS

Atopon Books
907 15th Street
Santa Monica, California 90403
United States

Publisher's Cataloging-in-Publication data

Names: Barnes, Djuna, author.
Title: A Book/ Djuna Barnes.
Description: Santa Monica, CA: Atopon Books, 2023.
Identifiers: LCCN: 2022943911 | ISBN: 979-8-9866109-9-3 (paperback) |
Subjects: LCSH Modernism (Literature. | Lesbianism in literature.
| BISAC FICTION / General | FICTION / LBGTQ+ / Lesbian |
FICTION / Romance / Polyamory
Classification: LCC PS3503.B26n 2023 | DDC 813.6--dc23

Cover Image: Djuna Barnes, "Sketch of a Woman with a Hat, Looking Right,"
for "The Terrorists," *New York Telegraph Sunday Magazine* (1917). The Djuna
Barnes Papers, Special Collections and University Archives, University of
Maryland.

Cover Credit: Brown Background / arlenta apostrophe / AdobeStock

Printed in the United States of America.

To
MOTHER

Introduction

Djuna Barnes: The Promise of Morbidity

When Djuna Barnes first published *A Book*, she was living with Thelma Wood, the love of her life, at 173, boulevard Saint-Germain, Paris. It was almost exactly one hundred years ago, during a hot and nearly rainless extended summer in 1923 – a rare halcyon period in Barnes' life. Although Barnes, 31 at the time, would later separate from Wood in a torturous breakup that inspired her best-known work, the 1936 novel *Nightwood*, the book you now hold in your hands represents the best of Barnes' early writing and marks an important shift in her career, from journalism to the world of capital-L "Literature." To read her work is to read her life, and to encounter every difficulty of reading along the way, including that posed by the intervention of biography.

Barnes was born in a log cabin on Storm King Mountain, which broods over the Hudson River about 50 miles north of New York City, on June 12, 1892, to parents Wald Barnes and Elizabeth Chappell. Their marriage lasted only 13 years; Wald was a bigamist who preached free love and free expression, luxuries afforded him by the relative financial success and stature of his mother, Zadel Barnes, who was in many ways the prototype for Djuna. Zadel was a writer and journalist whose radical energies and talents as a suffragist, labor reformist, and prohibitionist sent her first to Boston and then to London, where she made friends with Lady Wilde, introducing Oscar's mother to Karl Marx's daughter, Eleanor, before returning to America to support her own son. In similar fashion, Djuna's avidly creative youth led her to art school, which she dropped out of to pursue writing. Her prolific early career as a journalist, which began in Greenwich Village, sent her on assignment across Europe's bohemian enclaves and cultural capitals, including Paris and London, where her fiction writing blossomed. Like Zadel, Djuna met several luminaries of her day through her work and her wit – she became acquainted with and interviewed James Joyce, was partner (briefly) and benefactor (for years) to Baroness Elsa von Freytag-Loringhoven, had T.S. Eliot for an editor and constant correspondent, and was close friends with Mina Loy.

As biographer Philip Herring writes, although Barnes began writing professionally at 21 out of grave financial necessity to support her family – after her parents' divorce, Elizabeth was entirely dependent on her children and ex-mother-in-law – she arrived in the newspaper world with characteristic melodrama:

> One day, probably in the spring of 1913, clad in a calico dress and carrying a basket, and looking rather like a milkmaid gone astray, Djuna appeared at the *Brooklyn Daily Eagle*. She applied for a job, concluding with the simple statement: "You need me." Late in life, Djuna described this scene a bit differently to Chester Page, claiming that she said "she could draw and write and they would be foolish not to hire her." And so they did.[1]

For the most part, the early pieces that Barnes wrote as a freelance about-towner reflect this aplomb. They are wryly cynical, darkly funny, and creatively unfettered. An early article titled "What Is Good Form in Dying? In Which a Dozen Dainty Deaths Are Suggested for Daring Damsels" flippantly presents the proper hairstyles and fashions women might consider for the act of suicide, for example. And in her interviews with celebrities, minor and major, hailing mostly from the bohemian circles that she frequented in the Village, Barnes ignores the dutiful reportage of facts. Her pieces often read as if transplanted from the Decadent or Symbolist movements of

---

[1] Philip Herring, *Djuna: The Life and Work of Djuna Barnes* (New York: Viking Press, 1995): 75.

the late 19th century – art for art's sake winning out against the ethic of the by-line. Despite this, she occasionally wrote more serious critical pieces, too. In 1914, she even willfully underwent force-feeding – then commonly deployed against suffragettes on hunger strike – to report on the technique from the "inside." Her piece, "How it Feels to be Forcibly Fed," anticipates the anti-objective stance of New Journalism by about half a century, and catalogs the compounding ironies of a loss of agency – sociopolitical, physical, even spiritual – enacted by the state upon resistant bodies through the very medical system meant to maintain their health.

Barnes' remarkable life strongly influenced her fiction writing, too, which is rife with thinly veiled portraits, often satirical, of family, friends, and acquaintances. Her earliest standalone publication, *The Book of Repulsive Women: 8 Rhythms and 5 Drawings* (1915), offers unglamorous sketches that portray life among, and desire between, women on terms not unlike those of Charles Baudelaire's rag-pickers of the century before. And her later *Ladies Almanack* (1928) took such acute aim at personages then frequenting Natalie Clifford Barney's influential Parisian literary salon that Barnes felt it necessary to attribute the *Almanack* to "A Lady of Fashion" rather than signing her own name to it.[2] In 1928, Barnes published her first novel, *Ryder*, which details the sexual exploits of polygamist anti-hero Wendell Ryder (also called Jesus Mundane in the text) – a clear analog for Barnes' father Wald. Much of the novel's more explicit material – including the implied rape of the eldest daughter of Wendell's first wife – is obscured by its heavy and shifting stylization, which imitates French Renaissance writer François Rabelais' "vulgar" style of political satire, and although Barnes censored some material, the U.S. Postal Service initially refused to ship *Ryder* due to its bawdy illustrations.

Nowhere does Barnes' life stake its claim on her writing and its reception more fervently than in her best-known work, *Nightwood*, which established her as an outsider genius among the modernist elite of her day. It is a tour-de-force akin to Joyce's *Ulysses*, which

---

[2] As Herring notes in *Djuna*, "word got out rather quickly" about the true author of *Ladies Almanack*.

Barnes much admired, with its interpenetrating and porous narrative perspective that shifts between registers. In *Nightwood*, high camp and carnivalesque counterpoint almost painfully earnest spiritual exegesis, and breakup poetry of the finest order turns to mordant satire in the space of a page. A harlequin romance of defeated desire that is as opiate as it is impassioned, the novel traces the fitful passage of its protagonist, the somnambule Robin Vote – usually read as Thelma Wood, the Baroness Elsa von Freytag-Loringhoven, or both – as she carves successive, decaying erotic arcs in the American expatriate bohemian communities of early 20th century Paris and Vienna. Felix Volkbein, a pretend Baron based on Frederick Philip Grove, is first to attempt possession of Robin; Nora Flood, who stands in for Barnes herself, and Jenny Petherbridge (Henriette Alice McCrea-Metcalf) follow suit, though none succeed. Through the novel's fugue-like series of meetings and separations – in the hotels and bars of Paris, at the parties and circuses of Berlin and New York – wends Dr. Matthew-Mighty-grain-of-salt-Dante-O'Connor, Tiresian mother-confessor, self-styled gynaecologist, and first-class ranter whose excurses on "the night" offer little solace to Robin's lost lovers. Alternately hailed as "practically the only available expression of lesbian culture in the modern western world since Sappho" by Bertha Harris, and described as "a bleak picture of love between women" by Jeannette Winterson, *Nightwood* is divisively compelling, and has sustained several generations of scholarly exchange and popular appreciation. For better or worse, the novel reflects the patterns and passions of Barnes' life closely, allowing her to dwell in obsessive reimagination. As Barnes writes to her close friend Emily Coleman in July of 1936:

> I want to live. . .in the Hotel Recamier—where, in my book, Robin lived—tho Thelma never put her foot, in reality, over its steps—I haunt the Place St. Sulpice now, because I've made it in my book into my life—as if my life had really been there . . .I love what I have invented as much as that which fate gave me—a great danger for the writer perhaps. . .I come to love my

invention more—so am able—perhaps—only so able—to put Thelma aside—because now she is not Robin.[3]

Readers seeking deeper insight into the integuments of life and art so present in *Nightwood* will be both satisfied and disappointed by *A Book*. Much of *A Book* is adapted from writing that appeared in the earliest years of Barnes' career, during the 1910s and early 1920s. Of the twenty-six pieces of writing between its covers – twelve stories, eleven poems, and three plays – at least nine had appeared in print beforehand, in modernist "little magazines" like *The Little Review,* or in one of the several news publications that Barnes wrote for in New York. According to many critical accounts, as I will detail shortly, *A Book* makes a somewhat amateurish entry into the hodge-podge of avant-garde movements sweeping across Europe and America in the early 20th century. Barnes republished *A Book* twice after its initial appearance, though under different titles, first as *A Night Among the Horses* (1929) and then as *Spillway* (1962), revising, retitling, and cutting along the way from *A Book*'s twenty-six writings to just ten in *Spillway*. The result of *A Book*'s initially lukewarm reception, perhaps, these revisions also illuminate Barnes' complicated relationship with her writerly persona – alongside "A Lady of Fashion," Barnes often used the alias "Lydia Steptoe" to sign her journalism and dramatic pieces. As a kind of first-draft fictional memoir, then, this early work portends *Nightwood*'s decadent noir-ish mastery in halting, limited ways; though Barnes held on to *A Book* throughout her career, she held it at arm's length.

A Book's short stories and plays, which range from a few pages in length to no more than seventeen, often feature few characters, are heavy with dialogue, and exploit this structure to portray stilted, often viciously exploitative, economies of human difference. Among her common themes are: divides of class and status and the space between urban and rural sensibilities ("A Night Among the Horses," "Three from the Earth," "The Valet"); the differences of sexuality and gendered embodiment ("To the Dogs," "No-Man's-Mare," "The

---

3 Herring, 217.

Dove"); the relationships of always-precocious children to their guardians and older generations ("Oscar," "A Boy Asks a Question of a Lady"); and the "performance" of national and racial belonging ("The Rabbit," "Katrina Silverstaff," "The Nigger"). Every character study is clouded by pretensions to philosophical insight, and through the hills and valleys of this spiritual seeker-ism roam, as among inedible weeds, disinterested animals of a nature red in tooth and claw. "A Night Among Horses" opens *A Book* on all fours, with former-horse-lackey John crawling through the weeds outside of his betrothed, Freda Buckler's, mansion. Freda has outfitted John with top hat, frock coat, and pipe to "rise to General, or Lieutenant at least" (35) in a gender-swapped riff on George Bernard Shaw's *Pygmalion*. Drawn up resentfully out of his class position – "Was he a thing to be played with, debased into something better than he was—than he knew?" (34) – and perhaps unaware of Jane Collier's satirical 1753 *Essay on the Art of Ingeniously Tormenting* one's "superiors," John's spite sends him back to the weeds for a last encounter with his horses' hooves. John loses his life, and Buckler loses her puppet. In the play "Three from the Earth," the next entry in *A Book*, the Carson brothers, James, Henry, and John, "peasants of the most obvious type," visit the boudoir of Kate Morley, "[a]n adventuress, a lady of leisure" (40). The play tracks her violent emotional reversals as, wearing purple asters to impress, the boys come seeking letters from their dead father documenting his affair with Kate. She first savages their chthonic mien – "three columns of flesh without one of the five senses!" (49) – before begging self-consciously for their pardon: "Won't you have tea?—But no, pay no attention to me, that's another of my nasty malicious tricks. Curse life!" (51). These "three from the earth" become Kate's bad conscience incarnate, reproaching her with decidedly un-bumpkinesque diction when she asks how their father looked, in suicide: "You can't satisfy your aesthetic sense that way" (52). Barnes often humbles her human characters through unexpected reversals, repressed returns, and variations on "natural" comeuppance such as these.

The longer works of *A Book* continue in this vein to dramatize unexpected admixtures of aggression and tenderness that, Barnes seems to insist, lay beneath our social masks. This complicates the power relations of domination and subjugation that she obsessively explores, making her work both oddly contemporary and oddly estranged even from its own time. In "To the Dogs," the second play of the volume, Helena Hucksteppe refuses the advances of neighbor Gheid Storm, who "storms" her castle keep by striding through the window, a curious commonality in *A Book*. Hucksteppe anticipates the feminist killjoy – "I do not enjoy the spectacle of men ascending" (67) – and also plays the dominatrix, in Storm's folk fantasy – "there's a story that you come through once every Spring, driving a different man ahead of you with a riding whip" (67). The sexual politics of her scorn are further complicated by her strangely sympathetic handling of Storm's intrusion. Instead of "cancelling" Storm, Helena "entertains" his advances rather Socratically, reflecting his words back at him:

> STORM—It's strange to see a woman like you turning to
>   the merely bitter—
> HELENA—I began beyond bitterness.
> STORM—Why do you treat me this way?
> HELENA—How would you have me treat you? (68)

And a little later:

> STORM—You are not making anything easier.
> HELENA—I've never been callous enough to make things
>   easier.
> STORM—You're a queer woman—
> HELENA—Yes, that does describe me. (70)

More than self-preservation in the face of a potential sexual assault, Helena's rhetorical strategy offers her (and Barnes) a chance to play the killjoy, but also to explore the jouissance of the put-down. Indeed, we might read the erotic push-and-pull of "To the Dogs" – more wit than politics – for the ways it encodes much older literary styles, even if we can't help seeing it through the lens of the present.

The play seems to be stranded temporally in a backwards-looking riff on an as-yet-unwritten "Baby It's Cold Outside." It is as if Nell Gwyn were singing in *Neptune's Daughter* – Restoration satire meets the Great American Songbook. The enduring fondness for archaic styles which influenced Barnes' development as both a writer and a visual artist cannot be separated from her critical focus on sex and gender, as radically contemporary as that focus may seem at times.

As Daniela Caselli puts it, "Barnes is an improper modernist."[4] She did not do modernism right, that is; her writing was too out of sync, too obscure – too deranged, even – for her time or "period." Navigating between a nostalgia for outdated traditions and a desire to "make it new," as Ezra Pound's famous injunction urged the authorial elite, in 1928, to reinvent literature,[5] modernists like Barnes addressed a world whose own "newness" was dubious, violent, and unstable. In 1923, as anti-colonial movements around the world militated against recalcitrant imperial power, Europe was riven internally by the foment of fascism in new forms. Egyptian independence – Hitler's "Beer Hall Putsch" – the end of the Russian Civil War – the resurgence of the Ku Klux Klan – the founding of the Republic of Turkey – the Mandate for Palestine; conflicts ended, conflicts began. Sigmund Freud published *The Ego and the Id*; the Walt Disney Company was founded. Pancho Villa died; Charlton Heston was born. Modernists responded in kind to these new realities and absurdities. They staged abstract play-activism demonstrations for the public to protest nothing in particular. They wrote deeply committed works of political history and philosophical speculation in rarified language accessible only to select audiences. They rejected anything "bourgeois" and turned the world of "tradition" into a laboratory for experimental writing. Old genres were cut up and repurposed in idiosyncratic ways. "Realism," in art and writing, suffered several cuts, and died several deaths. New anti-traditions

4 Daniela Caselli, *Improper Modernism: Djuna Barnes's Bewildering Corpus* (Farnham: Ashgate Publishing, 2009): 2.

5 Pound's is, in fact, a recycled slogan from his reading of neo-Confucian scholar Chu Hsi (1130-1200 AD); see Michael North, *Novelty: A History of the New* (Chicago: Chicago UP, 2013): 162-163.

– polemical abstraction, parodical revision – grew up too fast and died young, without inheritors. A self-reflexive focus on the basic building blocks of art and writing – the materials being used and the institutional conditions of their use – reflected a broader self-consciousness of cultural conditions like the increase of industrialization, ongoing technological development, and the ideological inheritances of the European Enlightenment.

Even in the context of all this experimentation in the arts, Barnes' writing "performs an unmodern, unfashionable, unconventional, and inopportune modernism" according to Caselli (4), one at once too touched by the political advances of first- and second-wave feminism and yet too misogynist, too homophobic, too racist to count as progressive. There are several antisemitic character portraits in *A Book*, for example, and her characters are often given "ethnic" names for the sake of punning delight and nothing else, it seems.[6] The most challenging piece for today's reader in this context is likely "The Nigger," a story of a racist white Southern gentleman, John Hardaway, who is dying, and the black maid, Rabb, who stays by his bedside as he passes. Some scholars, like Jane Marcus, try to understand Barnes' engagements with race in terms of a broader focus on "difference" as such. Marcus reads the tattooed body of the black character Nikka in *Nightwood*, for example, as offering a kaleidoscopic critique of white fantasies of various orders: "I see the body of the Other. . .presented as a text in the novel, a book of communal resistances. . .in an endless play at dissolving and reconstituting difference" (86-90). Yet unlike in *Nightwood*, there is no diegetic reference to "writing" on the body of Rabb; instead, *A Book*

---

6 Philip Herring, editor, "Introduction," *Djuna Barnes: Collected Stories* (Los Angeles: Sun and Moon Press, 1996). Herring notes: "Although most of the characters in Barnes's stories are originally from Europe, in the early years she really didn't know much about the languages or cultures of her subjects; in fact, often their names do not reflect their national origins at all, or reveal no specific ethnicity. . .Several characters are not specifically named as Jewish, but are portrayed as such, among them the pawnbroker named Lydia Passova in "Mother." Of course, Passova as a Jewish surname is quite ludicrous" (9-10).

uses stereotype as a way to embolden itself, amplifying its curiosity about difference to the level of taboo. In the story, John repeatedly calls Rabb to tend him "with that hate a master calls love" (129), though his racist abuse of Rabb is mixed with half-forgotten nursery rhymes, feebly recited: "'Ah, my little one—I have held you on my knee—'I have kissed your ears and throat...'" (129). At one point, he tells Rabb to leave in order to eat, but she stays close, remaining in the corner of the room. This push-and-pull of violence and intimacy culminates in a seemingly sexual metaphor, and as John finally dies, Rabb gives him a "kiss":

> Suddenly Rabb bent down and leaning her mouth to his, breathed into him, one great and powerful breath. His chest rose, he opened his eyes, said 'Ah!' and died.
>
> Rabb ran her tongue along her lips, and raising her eyes, stared at a spot on the wall a little higher than she was wont to. After a while she remembered her unfinished soup (165)

Whether this "kiss" is meant to prolong John's life or seal his death is unclear; we are left with a scene of uncertain sexual "charge." Interracial marriage, cohabitation, and sex were not, of course, illegal in all parts of America at the time of this story's publication. Still, anti-miscegenation laws remained in effect throughout at least 29 states when *A Book* was printed, and the force of social prohibition maintained a powerful range. Barnes' tone in the story is not legal or political in the sense of a "public" discourse on race that we might expect from a more contemporary writer; instead she portrays race as one modality in an "erotic" of difference. The "satisfaction" of John Hardaway 's epiphanic or orgasmic "Ah!" in death, on the one hand, and the "dissatisfaction" of Rabb, who simply "stare[s] at a spot on the wall a little higher than she was wont to" (165), on the other, work at the boundaries of what is speakable or permissible in the context of American racial politics, as Barnes explores these taboos often for worse than for better.

The poetry of *A Book* largely offers a welcome respite from these challenges, and the collection's eleven poems are spaced rather evenly throughout the other material, perhaps in recognition of this fact. Some of the shortest poems – "Hush Before Love" and "Paradise," which are only five lines long apiece – might be passed over too quickly by readers, were it not for the sense that much of the verse in *A Book* operates in a kind of artificially separated holism. "Pastoral," the first poem, announces its titular theme as a balm after the particularly heavy story "Beyond the End," which tells of a wife, and her child born of adultery, returning to her husband after five years in medical care for tuberculosis. In contrast with the eschatological reflections on redemption these peculiarly human problems cause – the question of what, if anything, comes "beyond the end" – "Pastoral" follows a frog across the lawn, in politely rhyming iambic pentameter, and we meet cows and calves, fowl and mushrooms, a fox in the corn, as "[t]he seasons move forever, one on one" (l. 20, p. 90). Even the snails, adders, and lizards are rounded up with soothing magnanimity, as this "Pastoral" concludes with a rather much softer meditation on beginnings and ends: "Each is before, and each behind its time" (l. 36, p. 91). Though "Hush Before Love" and "Paradise" are decidedly parable-like in their animal focus, with the "Cock that Crew" and "Kiss that Slew" of "Paradise" recalling the Biblical betrayals of Peter and Judas, later poems "Song in Autumn" and "I'd Have You Think of Me" resume the natural immediacy of "Pastoral" in pleasantly "non-symbolic" earnest. "Song in Autumn" negotiates between a sense of protective gentleness for the speaker's love, "hid within the green / Long grasses" (ll. 2-3, p. 160) of the first stanza, and an environmental lament in the second, "All pulsing faintly, like a muted string / Above us where we weary of our vows—." In place of an aubade, we have a nocturne whose meditative intensity, unlike some of *A Book*'s other nature scenes, does not succumb to the deflating effects of a witticism or appear to be shaping itself into a mock proverb. At moments like this, Barnes approaches a 19th-century Romantic seriousness while signaling the return of animism in mid-20th-century American poets like John Ashbery or Sylvia Plath. Perhaps somewhere, among "the dusk [that] steals up between / Each leaf" (ll. 3-4, p. 160), Walt Whitman lurks in the shade. These ruminations on nature largely work as light interludes in harmony with each other, even if they are somewhat discordant among *A Book*'s heavier fiction and drama.

Other poems, such as "Six Songs of Khalidine," offer variations on the pastoral theme. "Khalidine" is dedicated to Mary Pyne, a one-time coworker of Barnes' at the *New York Press* and actor with the Provincetown Players, with whom Barnes became enamoured, leaving fruit baskets on her doorstep for Pyne's father to kick away disapprovingly. When Pyne died young of tuberculosis in 1919, Barnes attended her deathbed and even tried to claim her body for right of burial.[7] As Sarah Parker has pointed out, the poem's fetishization of Pyne, and the "flame of [her] red hair [which] does crawl and creep / Upon [her] body that denies the gloom" (ll. 1-2, p. 136), reproduces the 19th-century myth of Dante Gabriel Rossetti disinterring his muse Elizabeth Siddal's body, to find her hair still miraculously growing in the coffin.[8] In her reading of Barnes's *Repulsive Women*, Parker traces the troping-towards-suicide of young women in urban environments where they must become and perform their own sexual commodification to the point of disenchantment, exhaustion, and death. We might read *A Book*'s "Lullaby" in a similar vein, as a kind of synecdoche for the collection itself in its status as a memoir-in-progress, trending towards death. "Lullaby" describes key moments in its speaker's social and sexual development – a young girl, we can assume, as the poem oozes biography. In the first stanza, the young girl moves from sleeping "with a dog" (l. 1, 166) in a preview of *Nightwood*'s ending, perhaps, to running and playing leapfrog with the boys, to a same-sex repose: "Now it is a girl's head that lies on my arm" (l. 4). The middle paragraph signals a moment of social uncertainty and stasis, referring perhaps to Barnes' provocative early journalism: "Now I dwell in Greenwich, and the people do not call; / Then I planted pepper-seed and stamped on

---

7 All information on the relationship between Pyne and Barnes is from Herring, *Djuna*, 73-74.

8 Sarah Parker, "Urban Economies and the Dead-Woman Muse," in *Economies of Desire at the Victorian Fin de Siècle: Libidinal Lives*, edited by Jane Ford, Kim Edwards Keates, and Patricia Pulham (New York: Routledge, 2017): 97-99.

them hard. / Now I am very quiet and I hardly plan at all" (ll. 6-8).
The "pepper-seed" might refer to her louder offerings in newsprint,
such as her piece on force-feeding, or perhaps some of the early fiction taking aim at her Village communities. There is alternately a
prophetic quality, too, to the third verse paragraph:

> Then I pricked my finger on a thorn, or a thistle,
> Put the finger in my mouth, and ran to my mother.
> Now I lie here, with my eyes on a pistol.
> There will be a morrow, and another, and another (ll. 9-12)

Barnes did in fact "run to her mother" in 1940, when, after
Nightwood's initial critical and public unsuccess, the alcoholism that
she had suffered for years became too destructive. Then patron-
ess Peggy Guggenheim uninstalled Djuna from her Devonshire
manor, sending her to live once more in upstate New York with
her mother, at that time a recent convert to Christian Science. The
poem evokes terminal irresolution; the pistol which would make an
end to boredom or dissatisfaction with life is contrasted with the
"morrows" that continue their irrepressible rebirth – "another, and
another" as a play on "mother." Though the poem's death-driving is
rather routine at this point in the reader's journey, the prophetic
quality here introduces a further twist on the symbolic range of
nature in *A Book*. Instead of installing "nature" as an impartial
reckoner of human folly or a parable for spiritual insight, Barnes
uses nature symbolism in "Lullaby" to mediate and obscure a shifting sense of self in social and literary space. As a *Künstlergedicht*,
or poem of artistic development, "Lullaby" manages the theme of
"career" in its many senses, in the sense of the speaker's progress
through the "institutions" of sex, family, and the broader artistic
communities of Greenwich Village and the Left Bank, but also in
the intransitive sense of their "careering" through this psychical and
sexual terrain in an uncontrolled way. In this context, the natural
references of "Lullaby" seem less concerned with "queer-coding" its
sexual content, for example, than with obfuscating what the twists
and turns of fate – of community both lost and found – might add

up to for the speaker, after all. To use Judith Butler's reading of Antigone from Sophocle's *Oedipus* and *Antigone*, we might call the speaker's resting pose in the poem one of "promising fatality." Like Antigone, who defies Creon's royal prohibition to claim death and burial rights for her kin – challenging the state's ideas of kinship and troubling conventional gender roles – the speaker of "Lullaby" seems to resist a full identification with normative ideas of sex, family, and power. Like Antigone, who, condemned to die, takes her own life, she also fails to escape them entirely. The uncertain ending of the poem, its flirtation with suicide and its erstwhile insistence that "life goes on" expresses this double-sense of being controlled by, while also controlling, the symbolic ties that bind us to social life. The thistle and the pistol illustrate by non-literal means, at least, Barnes' answer to the question posed her by Guido Bruno in a 1919 interview for *Pearson's Magazine*:

> I asked Djuna Barnes: "Why are you so dreadfully morbid?"
> "Morbid?" was her cynical answer. "You make me laugh. This life I write and draw and portray is life as it is, and therefore you call it morbid. Look at my life. Look at the life around me. Where is this beauty that I am supposed to miss? The nice episodes that others depict? Is not everything morbid?"[9]

Whether in poetry or the plain speech of an interview, biography is at times an impassable obstacle for Barnes' readers; her promising fatality finds no protective caul in any form.

Rounding out the volume are, appropriately, a series of sketch-like portraits that dot the constellation of the whole much like the poetry. "Six Songs of Khalidine" is accompanied by a study of Mary Pyne, as unflattering as the other portraits of *A Book*, but in line with Barnes' focus on the cruelty of nature and appearances, perhaps. As Herring writes about the drawings in *The Book of Repulsive Women*: "Hideous images are a Barnes stock-in-trade even in the later poems, but they focus on life in general as a dirty, mean

---

9 Barnes, Djuna. *Interviews*, edited by Alyce Barry and Douglas Messerli (Washington: Sun & Moon Press, 1985): 385, 386.

trick" (88). There is less to go off in *A Book*, whose isolated busts are more pensive, less satirical, than in *Repulsive Women*, where full figures of women are rendered in a decadent style reminiscent of Aubrey Beardsley's, with frills, flowers, and architectural abstractions interpenetrating the distorted human forms.[10] And there are no hints of the Tudor or French medieval influences that Barnes adapted for images in the later *Ryder* or *Ladies Almanack*. Still, those with an interest in tracing the development of Barnes as a graphic artist may find *A Book*'s sidestep into sketching compelling. Its five portraits are simple, dour, aggressive, skeptical, and imperious in turns, and perhaps beautiful in their catalogue of these unglamorous human shades. As Barnes' close friend Emily Coleman once wrote to her in 1935: "You make horror beautiful—it is your greatest gift."[11]

A Book's portraits, drawn from life but offering mean and meager insight, point to a strained, ambiguous relationship between Barnes and her art and writing that has frustrated readers for a long time. To write that *A Book* encountered mixed responses upon publication is to understate the point dramatically. It is a good thing that Barnes enjoyed gainful employment during this period; her relative success in the newspaper worlds of New York and Paris likely dulled the sting of *A Book*'s initial reviews. Digging into the archive of early 20th-century trade publications and literary journals reveals an unfortunate consensus on the overall effect of *A Book*: it is obscure, difficult, and certainly not for everyone. Writing for *Life* magazine in 1923, Dianne Warwick opines that "[a]n advertising man [sic] would be thoroughly justified in speaking of Miss Barnes's material and treatment as Something Different. . .The title of the collection is simply 'A Book,' and it's a smart choice, for I don't know what else it could have been called." Floyd Dell, a noted left-wing Greenwich intellectual and author, in an early-1924 review for *The Nation* titled "Irrelevant," carries this theme further: "Djuna Barnes is one of those writers, of a recent school, who defiantly

---

[10] Beardsley was also a caricaturist and cartoonist – a compelling parallel with Barnes' penchant for slice-of-life art and writing.
[11] Herring, *Djuna*, xvii.

refuse to find any sort of significance in the rank welter of life. Or so it would seem; the plain fact is that these stories are on the whole meaningless; the ascription of a highly philosophical intention to their meaninglessness is a mere critical guess." The most promising review is probably Burton Rascoe's in the Jan 6, 1924, issue of the *New York Times*, titled "Literary Pot-Pourri," and though the praise is centered on Barnes' delicate sensitivities, it cannot escape mention of her obscurity of perspective: "The thing that interests [Barnes] is the undercurrent of heart throbs which a phlegmatic world never senses. . .[she] has tried to catch some scintillation of the mind lost in the maze, all awry with the intricate adjustment to a world to which there seems no key. If she is unable to tell us what it is all about she has accomplished quite as much as the sages. . ."[12] By contrast, with flat diplomacy, *The Bookman*'s January 1924 issue, edited by John Farrar, states: "There is nothing here to suit many tastes."

Even friends and acquaintances found *A Book*'s contents stubbornly idiosyncratic. In a letter to Emily Coleman dated May 2, 1932, John Holms writes: "I read Djuna's first book of stories & sketches etc. recently: the most *unbelievable* junk, so bad I thought that by now she'd know & laugh about them (written 10 years or so ago when she was 30) but she thinks they are very good. Nothing but haughty misunderstood women pointing to the door, mixed up with a lot of. . .geniuses & intense, in its own way, but. . .sentimental romanticism"[13] Coleman's close relationship with Barnes extended beyond the personal to the professional, and it was Coleman who would convince T.S. Eliot, in his role as editor at Faber & Faber, to take on the final editing and publication of *Nightwood* after first editing it herself. Despite what the blistering misogyny of the above remarks might imply, Holms was a friend, too; he and Barnes spent several summers in the company of Peggy Guggenheim at Hayford Hall in Devonshire. The reputation of Barnes' early work within the broader New York literary subculture reveals much of the same treatment. Alexander Woollcott, part-time dramaturge

---

[12] Burton Rascoe, "Literary Pot-Pourri," *New York Times* 6 Jan. 1924, 14.
[13] Herring, 197.

and well-known critic, in a review of "Three from the Earth" from 1919 (the play was performed by the Provincetown Players, who mounted two other one-act plays by Barnes, before being included in *A Book*), offers underhanded praise: "'Three from the Earth' is enormously interesting, and the greatest indoor sport this week is guessing what it means. . .it is really interesting to see how absorbing and essentially dramatic a play can be without the audience ever knowing what, if anything, the author is driving at and without, as we have coarsely endeavored to suggest, the author knowing either."[14]

Despite these century-old misgivings, *A Book* offers many things to contemporary readers. Power and positionality are Barnes' constant focus throughout, and attitudes of political correctness are satirized as often as their anti-PC counterparts. Though her insensitivities, racist oversteps, and generally wicked view of human behavior present serious challenges, the ways in which she tests the limits of representation, even to the point of taboo, allow us to sharpen modern understandings of modernism's high-risk experiments with literary form and content. If contemporary reading practices, as Leo Bersani argues in *The Culture of Redemption*, want only to celebrate art for its power to "redeem" a life that is broken and oppressed, perhaps Barnes' "irredeemable" qualities as a writer are what make her most compelling. Those familiar with *Nightwood* will appreciate access to *A Book*'s seeming character studies for that later masterpiece, though the shorter experiments with mastery and non-mastery collected here will no doubt shock and repulse, at times, as they did a century ago for Barnes' first readers. If *A Book* is immature in many senses, it is a dynamic collection of immaturities, moving between genres and moods in a kind of frustrated virtuoso performance. It is by turns bleak and energetic, full of depressive musings and superb witticisms, the record of a mind alive to the paradoxes of modern life and of a writerly voice keen to be heard among those of her contemporaries. Though 1922-1923 was something of a "major"

---

14 Alexander Woollcott, "Second Thoughts on First Nights: The Provincetown Plays; The Inscrutable Authoress," *New York Times* 9 Nov. 1919, 22.

period for modernist literature – in 1922, Eliot's *The Wasteland* and Joyce's *Ulysses* appeared in book form for the first time; Jean Toomer's *Cane*, Kahlil Gibran's *The Prophet*, and an early version of Virginia Woolf's *Mrs. Dalloway* were published in 1923; at the end of that year, W.B. Yeats was awarded the Nobel Prize in Literature – Barnes' *A Book* sounds a note worth listening to, "minor" more in mood than stature, perhaps.

Barnes's last 40 years of life were spent reclusively at 5 Patchin Place, Greenwich Village, where she kept almost no friends and admitted even fewer visitors. She was especially recalcitrant with publishers and editors, repressing (unsuccessfully, in a few cases) reprintings of her work – it is highly unlikely she would have given her sanction to this book, for example.[15] Her career, which began in the light of art and writing, ended in the long shadow of her earlier achievements; Barnes wrote little during this long period, and started, but never finished, an autobiography. The "informal memoir" assembled by Frank O'Neal during the last years of her life – titled (after a morbid Hobbesian witticism of Barnes' own) *Life is Painful, Nasty & Short – In My Case It Has Only Been Painful and Nasty"* – was reviewed by *Publishers Weekly* in 1990 as "disorganized and inconclusive, providing just a few biographical tidbits and a smidgen of psychological speculation. Only confirmed Barnes enthusiasts are likely to be interested. Photos." Although the beauty and complexity of her creative work remains as a testament to her

---

[15] From a review of *Djuna Barnes: Collected Stories* by Peter Klappert for the Lambda Book Report in 1996: "Barnes spent the last decade of her life feeling besieged. She tried to get the feminist bookstore, Djuna Books, to change its name; she denied a mime troupe permission to do an interpretation of *Nightwood*; although she would not read the manuscript, Barnes vehemently opposed publication of my book of poems, *The Idiot Princess of the Last Dynasty* (an extended homage to *Nightwood* and to the Paris of the inter-war years). When Douglas Messerli, publisher of Sun & Moon Press, discovered that Barnes' early stories had gone out of copyright, she tried – and failed – to stop him from publishing them as *Smoke and Other Early Stories* (1982)."

passion and deep insight into life, her words to Robert Giroux, the American publisher of *The Antiphon*, in 1961 were perhaps true: "I have lived with suffering all my life, and I expect to do so until the day I die." Djuna Barnes died in her home on June 18, 1982, six days after her 90th birthday.

Torin McLachlan
University of British Columbia

Contents

Illustrations

A NIGHT AMONG THE HORSES

———

Toward dusk, in the Summer of the year, a man dressed in a frock coat and top hat, and carrying a cane, crept through the underbrush bordering the corral of the Buckler farm.

As he moved, small twigs snapped, fell and were silent. His knees were green from wounded shrubbery and grass, and his outspread hands tore unheeded plants. His wrists hurt him and he rested from time to time, always caring for his hat and knotted yellow cane, blowing through his moustache.

Dew had been falling, covering the twilight leaves like myriad faces damp with the perspiration of the struggle for existence, and half a mile away, standing out against the darkness of the night, a grove of white birches shimmered like teeth in a skull.

He heard the creaking of a gate, and the splashing of late rain into the depths of a dark cistern. His heart ached with the nearness of the earth, the faint murmur of it moving upon itself, like a sleeper who turns to throw an arm about a beloved.

A frog began moaning among the skunk cabbages, and John thrust his hand deep into his bosom.

Something somnolent seemed to be here, and he wondered. It was like a deep, heavy, yet soft prison where, without sin, one may suffer intolerable punishment.

Presently he went on, feeling his way. He reached a high plank fence and sensing it with his fingers, he lay down, resting his head against the ground.

He was tired, he wanted to sleep, but he searched for his hat and cane and straightened out his coat beneath him before he turned his eyes to the stars.

And now he could not sleep, and wondered why he had thought of it; something quick was moving the earth, it seemed to live, to shake with sudden immensity.

He heard a dog barking, and the dim light from a farm window kept winking as the trees swung against its square of light. The odor of daisies came to him, and the assuring, powerful smell of the stables; he opened his mouth and drew in his moustache.

A faint tumult had begun. A tremor ran under the length of his body and trembled off into the earth like a shudder of joy—died down and repeated itself. And presently he began to tremble, answering, throwing out his hands, curling them up weakly, as if the earth were withholding something precious, necessary.

His hat fell off, striking a log with a dull hollow sound, and he pressed his red moustache against the grass, weeping.

Again he heard it, felt it; a hundred hoofs beat upon the earth and he knew the horses had gone wild in the corral on the other side of the fence, for animals greet the Summer, striking the earth, as friends strike the back of friends. He knew, he understood; a hail to Summer, to life, to death.

He drew himself against the bars, pressing his eyes under them, peering, waiting.

He heard them coming up across the heavy turf, rounding the curve in the Willow Road. He opened his eyes and closed them again. The soft menacing sound deepened, as heat deepens, strikes through the skin into the very flesh. Head on, with long legs rising, falling, rising again, striking the ground insanely, like needles taking terrible, impossible and purposeless stitches.

He saw their bellies, fawn-coloured, pitching from side to side, flashing by, straining the fence, and he rose up on his feet and silently, swiftly, fled on beside them.

Something delirious, hysterical, came over him and he fell. Blood trickled into his eyes down from his forehead. It had a fine feeling for a moment, like a mane, like that roan mare's mane that had passed him—red and long and splendid.

He lifted his hand, and closed his eyes once more, but the soft pounding did not cease, though now, in his sitting position, it only jogged him imperceptibly, as a child on a knee.

It seemed to him that he was smothering, and he felt along the side of his face as he had done in youth when they had put a cap on him that was too large. Twining green things, moist with earth-blood, crept over his fingers, the hot, impatient leaves pressed in, and the green of the matted grass was deathly thick. He had heard about the freeness of nature, thought it was so, and it was not so.

A trailing ground pine had torn up small blades in its journey across the hill, and a vine, wrist-thick, twisted about a pale oak, hideously, gloriously, killing it, dragging it into dust.

A wax Patrick Pipe leaned against his neck, staring with black eyes, and John opened his mouth, running his tongue across his lips, snapping it off, sighing.

Move as he would, the grass was always under him, and the crackling of last Autumn's leaves and last Summer's twigs—minute dead of the infinite greatness—troubled him. Something portentous seemed connected with the patient noises about him. An acorn dropped, striking a thin fine powder out of a frail oak pod. He took it up, tossing it. He had never liked to see things fall.

He sat up, with the dim thunder of the horses far off, but quickening his heart.

He went over the scene he had with Freda Buckler, back there in the house, the long quivering spears of pot-grass standing by the window as she walked up and down, pulling at them, talking to him.

Small, with cunning fiery eyes and a pink and pointed chin. A daughter of a mother who had known too many admirers in her youth; a woman with an ample lap on which she held a Persian kitten or a trifle of fruit. Bounty, avarice, desire, intelligence—both of them had always what they wanted.

He blew down his moustache again thinking of Freda in her floating yellow veil that he had called ridiculous. She had not been angry, he was nothing but a stable boy then. It was the way with those small intriguing women whose nostrils were made delicate through the pain of many generations that they might quiver whenever they caught a whiff of the stables.

"As near as they can get to the earth," he had said, and was Freda angry? She stroked his arm always softly, looking away, an inner bitterness drawing down her mouth.

She said, walking up and down quickly, looking ridiculously small:

"I am always gentle, John"—frowning, trailing her veil, thrusting out her chin.

He answered: "I liked it better where I was."

"Horses," she said showing sharp teeth, "are nothing for a man with your bile—pot-boy—curry comber, smelling of saddle soap—lovely!" She shrivelled up her nose, touching his arm: "Yes, but better things. I will show you—you shall be a gentleman—fine clothes, you will like them, they feel nice." And laughing she turned on one high heel, sitting down. "I like horses, they make people better; you are amusing, intelligent, you will see—"

"A lackey!" he returned passionately, throwing up his arm. "What is there in this for you, what are you trying to do to me? The family—askance—perhaps—I don't know."

He sat down pondering. He was getting used to it, or thought he was, all but his wordy remonstrances. He knew better when thinking of his horses, realizing that when he should have married this small, unpleasant and clever woman, he would know them no more.

It was a game between them, which was the shrewder, which would win out? He? A boy of ill breeding, grown from the gutter, fancied by this woman because he had called her ridiculous, or for some other reason that he would never know. This kind of person never tells the truth, and this, more than most things, troubled him. Was he a thing to be played with, debased into something better than he was—than he knew?

Partly because he was proud of himself in the costume of a groom, partly because he was timid, he desired to get away, to go back to the stables. He walked up to the mirrors as if about to challenge them, peering in. He knew he would look absurd, and then knew, with shame, that he looked splendidly better than most of the gentlemen that Freda Buckler knew. He hated himself. A man who had grown out of the city's streets, a fine common thing!

She saw him looking into the mirrors, one after the other, and drew her mouth down. She got up, walking beside him in the end, between him and them, taking his arm.

"You shall enter the army—you shall rise to General, or Lieutenant at least—and there are horses there, and the sound of stirrups—with that physique you will be happy—authority you know," she said, shaking her chin, smiling.

"Very well, but a common soldier—"

"As you like—afterward."

"Afterward?"

"Very well, a common soldier."

He sensed something strange in her voice, a sort of irony, and it took the patience out of him:

"I have always been common, I could commit crimes, easily, gladly—I'd like to!"

She looked away. "That's natural," she said faintly; "it's an instinct all strong men have—"

She knew what was troubling him, thwarted instincts, common beautiful instincts that he was being robbed of. He wanted to do something final to prove his lower order; caught himself making faces, idiot faces, and she laughed.

"If only your ears stuck out, chin receded," she said, "you might look degenerate, common, but as it is—"

And he would creep away in hat, coat and with his cane, to peer at his horses, never daring to go in near them. Sometimes, when he wanted to weep, he would smear one glove with harness grease, but the other one he held behind his back, pretending one was enough to prove his revolt.

She would torment him with vases, books, pictures, making a fool of him gently, persistently, making him doubt by cruel means, the means of objects he was not used to, eternally taking him out of his sphere.

"We have the best collection of miniatures," she would say with one knee on a low ottoman, bringing them out in her small palm.

"Here, look."

He would put his hands behind him.

"She was a great woman—Lucrezia Borgia—do you know history—" She put it back because he did not answer, letting his mind, a curious one, torment itself.

"You love things very much, don't you?" she would question, because she knew that he had a passion for one thing only. She kept placing new ladders beneath his feet, only to saw them off at the next rung, making him nothing more than a nervous, irritable experiment. He was uneasy, like one given food to smell and not to taste, and for a while he had not wanted to taste, and then curiosity began, and he wanted to, and he also wanted to escape, and he could do neither.

Well, after he had married her, what then? Satisfy her whim and where would he be? He would be nothing, neither what he had been nor what other people were. This seemed to him, at times, her wish—a sort of place between lying down and standing up, a cramped position, a slow death. A curious woman.

This same evening he had looked at her attentively for the first time. Her hair was rather pretty, though too mousy, yet just in the nape of the neck, where it met the lawn of the collar it was very attractive. She walked well for a little woman, too.

Sometimes she would pretend to be lively, would run a little, catch herself at it, as if she had not intended to do it, and calm down once more, or creeping up to him, stroking his arm, talking to him, she would walk beside him softly, slowly, that he might not step out, that he would have to crawl across the carpet.

Once he had thought of trying her with honesty, with the truth of the situation. Perhaps she would give him an honest answer, and he had tried.

"Now, Miss Freda—just a word—what are you trying to do? What is it you want? What is there in me that can interest you? I want you to tell me—I want to know—I have got to ask someone, and I haven't anyone to ask but you."

And for a moment she almost relented, only to discover that she could not if she had wished. She did not know always what she meant herself.

"I'll tell you," she said, hoping that this, somehow, might lead her into the truth, for herself, if not for him, but it did not, "you are a little nervous, you will get used to it—you will even grow to like it. Be patient. You will learn soon enough that there is nothing in the world so agreeable as climbing, changing."

"Well," he said, trying to read her, "and then?"

That's all, you will regret the stables in the end—that's all." Her nostrils quivered. A light came into her eyes, a desire to defy, to be defied.

Then on this last night he had done something terrible, he had made a blunder. There had been a party. The guests, a lot of them, were mostly drunk, or touched with drink. And he, too, had too much. He remembered having thrown his arms about a tall woman, gowned in black with loose shoulder straps, dragging her through a dance. He had even sung a bit of a song, madly, wildly, horribly. And suddenly he had been brought up sharp by the fact that no one thought his behaviour strange, that no one thought him presumptuous. Freda's mother had not even moved or dropped the kitten from her lap where it sat, its loud resolute purr shaking the satin of her gown.

And he felt that Freda had got him where she wanted him, between two rungs. Going directly up to her, he said:

"You are ridiculous!" and twirled his moustache, spitting into the garden.

And he knew nothing about what happened until he found himself in the shrubbery, crawling toward the corral, through the dusk and the dampness of the leaves, carrying his cane, making sure of his hat, looking up at the stars.

Now he knew why he had come. He was with his horses again. His eyes, pressed against the bars, stared in. The black stallion in the lead had been his special pet, a rough animal, but kindly, knowing. And here they were once more, tearing up the grass, galloping about in the night like a ball-room full of real people, people who wanted to do things, who did what they wanted to do.

He began to crawl through the bars, slowly, deftly, and when half way through he paused, thinking.

Presently he went on again, and drawing himself into the corral, his hat and cane thrown in before him, he lay there mouth to the grass.

They were still running, but less madly; one of them had gone up the Willow Road leading into a farther pasture, in a flare of dust, through which it looked immense and faint.

On the top of the hill three or four of the horses were standing, testing the weather. He would mount one, he would ride away, he would escape. And his horses, the things he knew, would be his escape.

Bareback, he thought, would be like the days when he had taken what he could from the rush of the streets, joy, exhilaration, life, and he was not afraid. He wanted to stand up, to cry aloud.

And he saw ten or twelve of them rounding the curb, and he did stand up.

They did not seem to know him, did not seem to know what to make of him, and he stared at them wondering. He did not think of his white shirt front, his sudden arising, the darkness, their excitement. Surely they would know, in a moment more.

Wheeling, flaring their wet nostrils, throwing up their manes, striking the earth in a quandary, they came on, whinnied faintly, and he knew what it was to be afraid.

He had never been afraid and he went down on his knees. With a new horror in his heart he damned them. He turned his eyes up, but he could not open them. He thought rapidly, calling on Freda in his heart, speaking tenderly, promising.

A flare of heat passed his throat and descended into his bosom.

"I want to live. I can do it—damn it—I can do it! I can forge ahead, make my mark."

He forgot where he was for a moment and found new pleasure in this spoken admission, this new rebellion. He moved with the faint shaking of the earth, like a child on a woman's lap.

The upraised hoofs of the first horse missed him, but the second did not.

And presently the horses drew apart, nibbling here and there, switching their tails, avoiding a patch of tall grass.

THREE FROM THE EARTH

———

PERSONS:
    JAMES | CARSON brothers
    HENRY   "
    JOHN   "

KATE MORLEY | An adventuress, a lady of leisure

TIME—Late afternoon

PLACE—KATE MORLEY'S boudoir. A long narrow room, with a great many lacquer screens in various shades of blue, a tastefully decorated room though rather extreme.

At the rise of the curtain the three CARSON brothers are discovered sitting together on a couch to the left. They look like peasants of the most obvious type. They are tall, rather heavy—and range in age from nineteen to twenty-five. They have sandy, sun-bleached hair that insists upon sticking straight up—oily, sweaty skins—large hanging lips and small eyes on which a faint whitish down moves for lashes. They are clumsy and ill clothed. Russet shoes are on all six feet. They each wear a purple aster and each has on a tie of the super-stunning variety—they have evidently done their best to be as one might say "well dressed."

When they speak—aside from their grunts—their voices are rough, nasal and occasionally crack. They are stoop-shouldered and their hands are excessively ugly.

Yet in spite of all this, their eyes are intelligent, their smiles gentle, melancholy, compassionate. And though they have a look of formidable grossness and stupidity, there is, on second observation, a something beneath all this in no way in keeping with this first impression.

JOHN, the youngest, and the smallest, looks around the room carefully.

JOHN—A nice room, eh? [*He tries to whisper, but it comes forth buzzing and harsh.*]

JAMES—A woman's room.

HENRY—How?

JAMES—A narrow room, John.

JOHN—Well?

JAMES—Cats and narrow walls.

HENRY—[*Grunting*] Ugh.

JOHN—Hush—I hear her coming! [*The curtains part and KATE MORLEY enters. She is a woman of about forty. Handsome. Dark. She is beautifully dressed—in a rather seductive fashion. She has a very interesting head; she has an air of one used to adulation and the pleasure of exerting her will. She has a trick of narrowing her eyes. As she comes forward there is a general commotion among the brothers, but none manages to stand up.*]

KATE—Good day, gentlemen.

ALL THREE—Good day.

KATE—Nice of you to call on me. [*She seats herself, crossing her legs.*] You are the three Carsons, John, James and Henry, aren't you? I haven't seen you for years, yet I think I should have known you.

ALL THREE—Ah ha.

KATE—Yes, I presume I should have known you. I have a good memory. Well, as I said, it's nice of you to come to see me. Social?

HENRY—You might call it that.

KATE—It's quite nice to get an unexpected visitor or so. I'm the kind of woman who knows just who is going to call on Monday, Tuesday, Thursday—

ALL THREE—Ah ha.

KATE—How's the country?

JOHN—Just the same.

KATE—It always is.—Don't you go mad—watching it?

HENRY—Now and again.

KATE—And how's your father? [*Not pausing for an answer—almost to herself.*] I remember—*he* was always mad. He used to wear a green cloth suit, and he carried white rats all over his shoulders. [*Remembering the three.*] Ah, yes, your father—he was a barber, wasn't he?

HENRY—No, a chemist.

KATE—[*Laughing uneasily.*] I have a bad memory after all. Well, anyway, in those days he had begun to be queer—everyone noticed it—even that funny man who had those three flaxen-haired daughters with the thin ankles who lived at the end of the street—and your mother—a prostitute, I believe.

HENRY—[*Calmly.*] At times.

KATE—A dancing girl without a clean word in her vocabulary, or a whole shirt to her name—

JAMES—But a woman with fancies.

KATE—[*Sarcastically.*] And what ability?

HENRY—Oh, none, just a burning desire.

KATE—What's the use of going into that? How did you get here—what for?

ALL THREE—On bicycles.

KATE—[*Bursting into laughter.*] How exactly ridiculous and appropriate—and what else?

JOHN—To see how the sun falls in a place like this.

KATE—[*Angrily, rising.*] Well, you see, from left to right, and right to left—

HENRY—True.

JOHN—[*Quietly.*] And we wanted to see how you walked, and sat down, and crossed your legs—

HENRY—And to get father's letters.

KATE—Well, you see how I walk, sit down, cross my legs. What letters?

JAMES—Letters to you.

KATE—[*Uneasily.*] So you know about that—well, and what would you fellows do with them—read them to see how clever they are?

JAMES—No, we have the clever ones.

KATE—Mine?

JOHN and HENRY—[*Nodding.*] Exactly.

KATE—Oh!

JOHN—You suffer?

KATE—From time to time—there's always a reaction.

HENRY—That's vulgar, isn't it?

KATE—Not unusually.

JOHN—The letters?

KATE—[*To herself.*] Well, there is malice in me—what of it? We've all been a while with the dogs, we don't all learn to bark.

JOHN—Ah ha.

KATE—See here, what will you do with your father's letters?

HENRY—Destroy them, perhaps.

KATE—And if I give them to you—will your father be as generous with mine?

HENRY—Father is undoubtedly a gentleman—even at this moment.

KATE—Well, we shall see about that—first tell me how you live.

JOHN—We go down on the earth and find things, tear them up, shaking the dirt off. [*Making motions to illustrate.*] Then there are the cows to be milked, the horses—a few—to be fed, shod and curried—do you wish me to continue?

KATE—Yes, yes, go on.

HENRY—[*Taking the tale up.*] We get up at dawn, and our father turns over in bed and whispers: "If you meet anyone, say nothing; if you are asked a question, look stupid—"

KATE—I believe you.

JAMES—And he says: "Go about your work as if you had neither sight, speech nor hearing—"

KATE—Yes—

JOHN—And he adds: "If you should meet a woman in the road—"

KATE—[*Excited.*] Then what?

HENRY—That's enough. Then of a Sunday we watch the people going to church, when we hear the "Amen," we lift a little and sit back—and then again—

KATE—Religion?

HENRY—Enough for our simple needs.

KATE—Poor sheep!

JAMES—Wise sheep!

KATE—What! Well perhaps. No one is any longer sure of anything. Then what?

JOHN—When we come home he says: "What have you seen and heard today?" He never asks, "What have you said?"

KATE—He trusts you?

JOHN—Undoubtedly. Sometimes we say, "We saw a hawk flying," or, "A badger passed," and sometimes we bring him the best treat of all—

KATE—Well?

JOHN—Something dead.

KATE—Dead?

HENRY—Anything that has destroyed the crops—a mole—a field-mouse.

KATE—And never anything that's harmless?

JOHN—Never.

KATE—Well, see here, I'll give you those letters. Suddenly my heart says to me, "Kate, give the oxen the rope, they won't run away."—Isn't it so? Very well, I put my hand on a certain package and all is over—I'm about to be married, you know. [*She has risen and gone over to a little box standing on the desk. Out from this she takes a package of letters tied with a red ribbon. She turns and walks straight up to* JOHN.] I'll give them to you. You are the youngest, the gentlest, and you have the nicest hands. [*She sits down, breathing with difficulty.*]

JOHN—[*Putting them into his blouse.*] Thank you, Kate Morley.

KATE—Now, tell me about everything. How is that mother of yours? I remember her—she was on the stage—she danced as they say, and she sang. She had a pet monkey—fed it honey out of a jar kept full by her admirers: grooms, stage hands, what not—

HENRY—Yes, and she used to draw pictures of it in the style of Dürer—almost morbid—and later it caught a disease and died—

KATE—I don't doubt it—and she, she had an under-lip like a balloon—and your father kissed that mouth, was even tempted—

JAMES—My father often saw beyond the flesh.

KATE—Kissed such a creature!

HENRY—At such times she was beautiful.

KATE—[*With a touch of humility.*] Yes, I'm sorry—I remember. Once I passed her, and instead of saying something, something horrible—she might—she looked down.

JOHN—She was beautiful, looking down.

KATE—[*Angry.*] And I, I suppose I wasn't beautiful to look at—

HENRY—No, I suppose not, that is, not for her.

KATE—[*Viciously.*] Well, let me tell you, you haven't inherited her beauty. Look at your hands—thick, hard, ugly—and the life lines in them like the life lines in the hands of every laborer digging sewers—

JOHN—There's something in that, but they are just beginning.

KATE—[*Turning on them.*] Look at you! You're ugly, and clumsy, and uncouth. You grunt and roar, you wear abominable clothes—and you have no manners—and all because of your father, your mighty righteous and original father. You don't have to be like this. You needn't have little pigs' eyes with bleached lashes, and thick hanging lips—and noses—but I suppose you've got adenoids, and you may suffer from the fact that your mother had a rupture, and in all probability you have the beginning of ulcers of the stomach, for God knows your father couldn't keep a meal down like a gentleman!

HENRY—He *was* delicate.

KATE—And why was he delicate? He called himself "The little Father," as one might say, "The great Emperor." Well, to have a father to whom you can go and say, "All is not as it should be"—that would have been everything. But what could you say to him, and what had he to say to you? Oh, we all have our pathetic moments of being at our best, but he wasn't satisfied with that, he wanted to be at it all the time. And the result, the life of a mole. "Listen and say nothing." Then he becomes the gentleman farmer because he discovers he cannot be the Beloved Fool. Suddenly he is the father of three creatures for all the world like Russian peasants—without an idea, a subtlety—it's wicked, that's all, wicked—and as for that, how do you know but that all three of you had a different mother? Why, great God, I might be the mother of one of you!

JOHN—[*Significantly.*] So I believe, madam.

KATE—[*Unheeding.*] Do you think a man like your father had any right to bring such children as you into the world—three columns of flesh without one of the five senses! [*She suddenly buries her head in her hands.*]

JOHN—[*Gently.*] You loved our father.

HENRY—And you also had your pot of honey—

KATE—Thank God I had no ideals—I had a religion.

JOHN—Just what?

KATE—You wouldn't understand.

HENRY—Shoes to the needy?

KATE—No, I'm not that kind, vicious boy.

JOHN—Are you quite certain?

KATE—I'll admit all my candles are not burning for God. Well, then, blow them out, still I'll have a light burning somewhere, for all your great breaths, you oxen!

HENRY—You were never a tower builded of ivory—

KATE—You're too stupid to be bitter—your voices are too undeveloped—you'd say "love" and "hate" the same way.

JAMES—True, we have been shut away from intonations.

KATE—You wouldn't even wish to die.

JOHN—We shall learn.

KATE—Why bother?

John—[*Abruptly rising.*] You have posed for the madonna?

KATE—Every woman has.

JOHN—You have done it better than most.

KATE—What do you mean?

JOHN—I looked at it when I came in. [*He picks up the photograph.*]

KATE—Let it be—I was playing in the "Crown of Thorns," an amateur theatrical.

JOHN—Yes, I presumed it was amateur—

JAMES—You were a devoted mother?

KATE—I have no virtues.

HENRY—And vices?

KATE—Weak in one, weak in the other.

JOHN—However, the baby had nice hands—

KATE—[*Looking at him.*] That is true.

JAMES—But then babies only use their hands to lift the breast, and occasionally to stroke the cheek—

KATE—Or throw them up in despair—not a heavy career.

JOHN—And then?

KATE—[*In an entirely new tone.*] Won't you have tea?— But no, pay no attention to me, that's another of my nasty malicious tricks. Curse life!

HENRY—Your life is drawing to a close.

JAMES—And from time to time you place your finger on a line of Nietzsche or Schopenhauer, wondering: "How did he say it all in two lines?" Eh?

KATE—As you say. [*She looks at them slowly, one by one.*] You are strange things. [*Coming back.*] But at least I've given up something— look at your mother, what did she give up for your father—a drunken husband—

JAMES—A drunken lover—that's different.

KATE—I can't help thinking of that great gross stomach of hers.

JAMES—Gross indeed, it won't trouble him any more.

KATE—What's that?

JOHN—He cut his throat with a knife—

KATE—Oh, my God! [*Pause.*] How did he look?

JOHN—You can't satisfy your æsthetic sense that way—he looked— well, ugly, played out; yes, played out. Everything had been too much for him—you—us—you could see that in the way he—

KATE—[*In a whisper.*] Well, that's strange—everything seems—I knew him, you know. [*She begins to laugh.*] And the dogs barked?

JAMES—So I believe.

KATE—[*Dazed.*] And you, what are you three going to do?

HENRY—We are coming out of the country—we are going abroad—we can listen there.

KATE—Abroad—listen—what are you saying?

HENRY—There are great men abroad.

JAMES—Anatole France, De Gourmont—

KATE—De Gourmont is dead.

JOHN—There will be others.

KATE—[*Still dully.*] And how did you come to know such names—oh, your father, of course—

JOHN—We needed them.

KATE—Strange, I've been prepared for every hour but this—

JAMES—Yet I dare say you've never cried out.

KATE—You are mistaken. I've cried: "To the evil of mind all is evil—"

HENRY—Ah ha, and what happened?

KATE—Sometimes I found myself on my knees—

JAMES—And sometimes?

KATE—That's enough, haven't we about cleared all the shavings out of the carpenter shop?

HENRY—You at least will never kill yourself.

KATE—Not likely, I'll probably die in bed with my slippers on— you see, I have a pretty foot.

HENRY—We understand—you are about to be married.

KATE—To a supreme court judge—so I'm cleaning house.

JOHN—[*Standing with the photograph.*] But it won't be quite cleared out until this goes. [*He takes it out of the frame and turning it over . . .reads.*] "Little John, God bless him." [*He turns it back.*] God bless him. Well, just for that I'd like to keep it.

KATE—That's my affair.

JOHN—So I see. [*He puts the photo in his blouse with the letters.*]

KATE—Well, perhaps—well, you're not so stupid after all— Come, for the madonna give me back the letters—I'll burn them I swear, and you can put the madonna at the foot of the bed.

JOHN—I shan't put it at the foot of the bed—I don't look at the foot of the bed—

HENRY and JAMES—[*Rising.*] And now we shall go.

KATE—[*Her hands to her head.*] But, gentlemen, gentlemen—

HENRY—We won't need to bother you again. We are leaving the country and going elsewhere—and there was only one of us to whom you might have shown a little generosity—in other words we do not wish to be reminded, and now we can forget, and in time become quite hilarious—

KATE—But, gentlemen, gentlemen, not this way—

JOHN—Well? [*Quite suddenly he takes her in his arms, raises her face and kisses her on the mouth.*]

KATE—[*Crying out.*] Not that way! Not that way!

JAMES—That's the way you bore him!

[*The curtain drops behind them.*]

THE VALET

———

The fields about Louis-Georges' house grew green in early Spring, leaving the surrounding country in melancholy grey, for Louis-Georges was the only man who sowed his ground to rye.

Louis-Georges was of small stature. His face was oblong, too pale. A dry mouth lay crookedly beneath a nose ending in a slight bulb. His long animal-like arms swung half a rhythm ahead of his legs.

He prided himself on his farming, though he knew nothing about it. He surveyed the tender coming green with kindly good nature, his acres were always a month ahead of his neighbours'.

Sometimes standing in the doorway, breathing through the thick hair in his nostrils, stretching his gloves, he would look at the low-lying sheds and the stables and the dull brown patches of ploughed earth, and mutter, "Splendid, splendid!"

Finally he would stroll in among the cattle where, in dizzy circles, large coloured flies swayed, emitting a soft insistent drone, like taffeta rubbed against taffeta.

He liked to think that he knew a great deal about horses. He would look solemnly at the trainer and discuss length of neck, thinness and shape of flank by the hour, stroking the hocks of his pet racer. Sometimes he would say to Vera Sovna: "There's more real breeding in the rump of a mare than in all the crowned heads of England."

Sometimes he and Vera Sovna would play in the hay, and about the grain bins. She in her long flounces, leaping in and out, screaming and laughing, stamping her high heels, setting up a great commotion among her ruffles.

Once Louis-Georges caught a rat, bare-handed, and with such skill that it could not bite. He disguised his pride in showing it to her by pretending that he had done so to inform her of the rodent menace to Winter grain.

Vera Sovna was a tall creature with thin shoulders; she was always shrugging them as if her shoulder-blades were heavy. She dressed in black and laughed a good deal in a very high key.

She had been a great friend of Louis-Georges' mother, but since her death she had fallen into disrepute. It was hinted that she was "something" to Louis-Georges; and when the townsfolk and neighbouring landholders saw her enter the house they would not content themselves until they saw her leave it.

If she came out holding her skirts crookedly above her thin ankles, they would find the roofs of their mouths in sudden disapproval, while if she walked slowly, dragging her dress, they would say: "See what a dust Vera Sovna brings up in the driveway; she stamps as if she were a mare."

If she knew anything of this feeling, she never showed it. She would drive through the town and turn neither to right nor left until she passed the markets with their bright yellow gourds and squashes, their rosy apples and their splendid tomatoes, exhaling an odour of decaying sunlight. On the rare occasions when Louis-Georges accompanied her, she would cross her legs at the knee, leaning forward, pointing a finger at him, shaking her head, laughing.

Sometimes she would go into the maids' quarters to play with Leah's child, a little creature with weak legs and neck, who always thrust out his stomach for her to pat.

The maids, Berthe and Leah, were well-built complacent women with serene blue eyes, quite far apart, and good mouths in which fine teeth grew gratefully and upon whom round ample busts flourished like plants. They went about their work singing or chewing long green salad leaves.

In her youth Leah had done something for which she prayed at intervals. Her memory was always taking her hastily away to kneel before the gaudy wax Christ that hung on a beam in the barn. Resting her head against the boards she would lift her work-worn hands, bosom-high, sighing, praying, murmuring.

Or she would help Berthe with the milking, throwing her thick ankles under the cow's udders, bringing down a sudden fury of milk, shining and splashing over her big clean knuckles, saying quietly, evenly:

"I think we will have rain before dawn."

And her sister would answer: "Yes, before dawn."

Leah would spend hours in the garden, her little one crawling after her, leaving childish smears on the dusty leaves of the growing corn, digging his hands into the vegetable tops, falling and pretending to have fallen on purpose; grinning up at the sun foolishly until his eyes watered.

These two women and Louis-Georges' valet, Vanka, made up the household, saving occasional visits from Louis-Georges' aunts, Myra and Ella.

This man Vanka was a mixture of Russian and Jew. He bit his nails, talked of the revolution, moved clumsily.

His clothes fitted him badly, he pomaded his hair, which was reddish yellow, pulled out the short hairs that tormented his throat, and from beneath his white brows distributed a kindly intelligent look. The most painful thing about him was his attempt to seem alert, his effort to keep pace with his master.

Louis-Georges would say, "Well now, Vanka, what did they do to you in Russia when you were a boy?"

"They shot my brother for a red," Vanka would answer, pulling the hairs. "They threw him into prison, and my sister took him his food. One day our father was also arrested, then she took two dinner pails instead of one. Once she heard a noise, it sounded like a shot, and our father returned her one of the pails. They say he looked up at her like a man who is gazed at over the shoulder." He had told the tale often, adding: "My sister became almost bald later on, yet she was a handsome woman; the students used to come to her chambers to hear her talk."

At such times Louis-Georges would excuse himself and shut himself up to write, in a large and scrawling hand, letters to his aunts with some of Vanka's phrases in them.

Sometimes Vera Sovna would come in to watch him, lifting her ruffles, raising her brows. Too, she would turn and look for a long time at Vanka who returned her look with cold persistence, the way of a man who is afraid, who does not approve, and yet who likes.

She would stand with her back to the fireplace, her high heels a little apart, tapping the stretched silk of her skirt, saying:

"You will ruin your eyes," adding: "Vanka, won't you stop him?"

She seldom got answers to her remarks. Louis-Georges would continue, grunting at her, to be sure, and smiling, but never lifting his eyes: and as for Vanka he would stand there, catching the sheets of paper as they were finished.

Finally Louis-Georges would push back his chair, saying: "Come, we will have tea."

In the end he fell into a slow illness. It attacked his limbs, he was forced to walk with a cane. He complained of his heart, but he persisted in going out to look at the horses, to the barn to amuse Vera Sovna, swaying a little as he watched the slow-circling flies, sniffing the pleasant odours of cow's milk and dung.

He still had plans for the haying season, for his crops, but he gave them over to his farm hands, who, left to themselves, wandered aimlessly home at odd hours.

About six months later he took to his bed.

His aunts came, testing with their withered noses the smell of decaying wood and paregoric, whispering that "he never used to get like this."

Raising their ample shoulders to ease the little black velvet straps that sunk into their flesh, they sat on either side of his bed.

They looked at each other in a pitifully surprised way. They had never seen illness, and death but once—a suicide, and this they understood: one has impulses, but not maladies.

They were afraid of meeting Vera Sovna. Their position was a difficult one; having been on friendly terms while Louis-Georges' mother lived, they had nevertheless to maintain a certain dignity and reserve when the very townsfolk had turned against her. Therefore they left her an hour in the evening to herself. She would come creeping in, saying:

"Oh, my dear," telling him long unheard stories about a week she had spent in London. A curious week, full of near adventure, with amusing tales of hotel keepers, nobility. And sometimes leaning close to him, that he might hear, he saw that she was weeping.

But in spite of this and of his illness and the new quality in the air, Vera Sovna was strangely gay.

During this illness the two girls served as nurses, changing the sheets, turning him over, rubbing him with alcohol, bringing him his soup, crossing themselves.

Vanka stood long hours by the bedside coughing. Sometimes he would fall off into sleep, at others he would try to talk of the revolution.

Vera Sovna had taken to dining in the kitchen, a long bare room that pleased her. From the window one could see the orchards and the pump and the long slope down to the edge of the meadow. And the room was pleasant to look upon. The table, like the earth itself, was simple and abundant.

It might have been a meadow that Leah and Berthe browsed in, red-cheeked, gaining health, strength.

Great hams, smoked fowl with oddly taut legs hung from the beams, and under these the girls moved as if there were some bond between them.

They accepted Vera Sovna's company cheerfully, uncomplainingly, and when she went away they cleared up her crumbs, thinking and talking of other things, forgetting.

Nothing suffered on account of his illness. The household matters went smoothly, the crops ripened, the haying season passed, and the sod in the orchards sounded with the thud of ripe falling fruit. Louis-Georges suffered alone, detached, as if he had never been. Even about Vera Sovna there was a strange quiet brilliancy, the brilliancy of one who is about to receive something. She caressed the medicine bottles, tended the flowers.

Leah and Berthe were unperturbed, except from overwork; the face of Vanka alone changed.

He bore the expression at once of a man in pain and of a man who is about to come into peace. The flickering light in Louis-Georges' face cast its shadow on that of his valet.

Myra and Ella became gradually excited. They kept brushing imaginary specks of dust from their shoulders and bodices, sending each other in to observe him. They comforted themselves looking at him, pretending each to the other that he was quite improved. It was not so much that they were sorry to have him die, as it was that they were not prepared to have him die.

When the doctor arrived they shifted their burden of worry. They bought medicine with great relish, hurriedly. Finally to lessen the torment they closed their eyes as they sat on either side of his bed, picturing him already dead, laid out, hands crossed, that they might gain comfort upon opening them, to find him still alive.

When they knew that he was really dying they could not keep from touching him. They tried to cover him up in those parts that exposed too plainly his illness: the thin throat, the damp pulsing spot in the neck. They fondled his hands, driving doctor and nurse into a passion.

At last, in desperation, Myra knelt by his bed, touched his face, stroked his cheeks, trying to break the monotonous calm of approaching death.

Death did not seem to be anywhere in him saving in his face ...it seemed to Myra that to drive it from his eyes would mean life. It was then that she and her sister were locked out, to wander up and down the hall, afraid to speak, afraid to weep, unless by that much they might hasten his death.

When he finally died, they had the problem of Vera Sovna.

But they soon forgot her, trying to follow the orders left by the dead man. Louis-Georges had been very careful to see to it that things should go on growing; he had given many orders, planned new seasons, talked of "next year," knowing that he would not be there.

The hens cackled with splendid performances, the stables resounded with the good spirits of the horses, the fields were all but shedding their very life on the earth as Vanka moved noiselessly about, folding the dead man's clothes.

When the undertaker arrived Vanka would not let him touch the body. He washed and dressed it to suit himself. It was he who laid Louis-Georges in the shiny coffin, it was he who arranged the flowers, and he who finally left the room on the flat of his whole noisy feet for the first time in years. He went to his own room overlooking the garden.

He paced the room. It seemed to him that he had left something undone. He had loved service and order; he did not know that he also loved Louis-Georges, who made service necessary and order desirable.

This distressed him, he rubbed his hands, holding them close to his mouth, as if by the sound of one hand passing over the other he might learn some secret in the stoppage of sound.

Leah had made a scene, he thought of that. A small enough scene, considering. She had brought her baby in, dropping him beside the body, giving the flat-voiced: "Now you can play with him a minute."

He had not interfered, the child had been too frightened to disturb the cold excellence of Louis-Georges' arrangement, and Leah had gone out soon enough in stolid silence. He could hear them descending the steps, her heavy slow tread followed by the quick uneven movements of the child.

Vanka could hear the rustling of the trees in the garden, the call of an owl from the barn; one of the mares whinnied and, stamping, fell off into silence.

He opened the window. He thought he caught the sound of feet on the pebbles that bordered the hydrangea bushes; a faint perfume, such as the flounces of Vera Sovna exhaled, came to him. Irritated, he turned away, when he heard her calling.

"Vanka, come, my foot is caught in the vine."

Her face, with wide hanging lips, came above the sill, and the same moment she jumped into the room.

They stood looking at each other. They had never been alone together before. He did not know what to do.

She was a little dishevelled, twigs from the shrubbery clung to the black flounces of her gown. She raised her thin shoulders once, twice, and sighed.

She reached out her arm, whispering:

"Vanka."

He moved away from her, staring at her.

"Vanka," she repeated, and came close, leaning a little on him.

In a voice of command, she said simply, "You must tell me something."

"I will tell you," he answered, automatically.

"See, look at your hands—" She kissed them suddenly, dropping her wet lips into the middle of the palms, making him start and shiver.

"Look at these eyes—ah, fortunate man," she continued, "most fortunate Vanka; he would let you touch him, close, near the heart, the skin. You could know what he looked like, how he stood, how his ankle went into his foot." He ceased to hear her.

"And his shoulders, how they set. You dressed and undressed him, knew him, all of him, for many years—you see, you understand? Tell me, tell me what he was like!"

He turned to her. "I will tell you," he said, "if you are still, if you will sit down, if you are quiet."

She sat down with another sigh, with a touch of her old gaiety; she raised her eyes, watching him.

"His arms were too long, you could tell that—but beautiful, and his back was thin, tapering—full of breeding—"

TO THE DOGS

———

PERSONS:
  HELENA HUCKSTEPPE
  GHEID STORM—*Her neighbour*

TIME—*Late afternoon.*

PLACE—*In the mountains of Cornwall-on-Hudson—the* HUCK
  STEPPE *house.*

SCENE—*The inner room of the* HUCKSTEPPE *cottage.*

To the left, in the back wall, a large window overlooks a garden. Right centre, a door leads off into a bedroom, and from the bedroom one may see the woods of the mountain. The door is slightly open, showing a glimpse of a tall mirror and the polished pole of a bed.

In the right wall there is a fireplace.

A dog lies across the threshold, asleep, head on paws.

About this room there is perhaps just a little too much of a certain kind of frail beauty of object. Crystal glasses, scent bottles, bowls of an almost too perfect design, furniture that is too antiquely Beautiful.

HELENA HUCKSTEPPE, *a woman of about thirty-five, stands almost back view to the audience, one arm lying along the mantel. She is rather under medium in height. Her hair, which is dark and curling, is done carefully about a small fine head. She is dressed in a dark, long gown, a gown almost too faithful to the singular sadness of her body.*

At about the same moment as the curtain's rising, GHEID STORM *vaults the window-sill. He is a man of few years, a well-to-do man of property, brought up very carefully by upright women, the son of a conscientious physician, the kind of man who commutes with an almost religious fervour, and who keeps his wife and his lawns in the best possible trim, without any particular personal pleasure.*

GHEID *is tall, but much too honourable to be jaunty, he is decidedly masculine. He walks deliberately, getting all the use possible out of his boot-leather, his belt-strap and hat-bands.*

His face is one of those which, for fear of misuse, has not been used at all.

HELENA HUCKSTEPPE *does not appear to be in the least astonished at his mode of entrance.*

GHEID STORM—As you never let me in at the door, I thought of the window. [*HELENA remains silent.*] I hope I did not startle you. [*Pause.*] Women are better calm, that is, some kinds of calm—

HELENA—Yes?

GHEID—[*Noticing the dog, which has not stirred.*] You've got funny dogs, they don't even bark. [*Pause.*] I expected you'd set them on me; however, perhaps that will come later—

HELENA—Perhaps.

STORM—Are you always going to treat me like this? For days I've watched you walking with your dogs of an evening—that little black bullpup, and then those three setters—you've fine ways with you Helena Hucksteppe, though there are many tales of how you came by them—

HELENA—Yes?

STORM—Yes. [*Pause.*] You know, you surprise me.

HELENA—Why? Because I do not set my dogs on you?

STORM—Something like that.

HELENA—I respect my dogs.

STORM—What does that mean?

HELENA—Had I a daughter, would I set her on every man?

STORM—[*Trying to laugh.*] That's meant for an insult, isn't it? Well, I like the little insulting women—

HELENA—You are a man of taste.

STORM—I respect you.

HELENA—What kind of a feeling is that?

STORM—A gentleman's—

HELENA—I see.

STORM—People say of you: "She has a great many ways—"

HELENA—Yes?

STORM—[*Sitting on the edge of the table.*] "But none of them simple."

HELENA—Do they?

STORM—[*Without attempting to hide his admiration.*] I've watched your back: "There goes a fine woman, a fine silent woman; she wears long skirts, but she knows how to move her feet without kicking up a dust—a woman who can do that, drives a man mad." In town there's a story that you come through once every Spring, driving a different man ahead of you with a riding whip; another has it, that you come in the night—

HELENA—In other words, the starved women of the town are beginning to eat.

STORM—[*Pause.*] Well [*laughs*] I like you.

HELENA—I do not enjoy the spectacle of men ascending.

STORM—What are you trying to say?

HELENA—I'm saying it.

STORM—[*After an awkward pause.*] Do—you wish me to—go away?

HELENA—You will go.

STORM—Why won't you let me talk to you?

HELENA—Any man may accomplish anything he's capable of.

STORM—Do you know how I feel about you?

HELENA—Perfectly.

STORM—I have heard many things about your—your past—I believe none of them—

HELENA—Quite right, why should you mix trades?

STORM—What do you mean by that?

HELENA—Why confuse incapability with accomplishment—

STORM—It's strange to see a woman like you turning to the merely bitter—

HELENA—I began beyond bitterness.

STORM—Why do you treat me this way?

HELENA—How would you have me treat you?

STORM—There was one night when you seemed to know, have you forgotten? A storm was coming up, the clouds were rolling overhead—and you, you yourself started it. You kissed me.

HELENA—You say it was about to storm?

STORM—Yes.

HELENA—It even looked like rain?

STORM—Yes.

HELENA—[*Quickly in a different voice.*] It was a dark night, and I ended it.

STORM—What have I done?

HELENA—You have neglected to make any beginning in the world—can I help that?

STORM—I offer you a clean heart.

HELENA—Things which have known only one state, do not interest me.

STORM—Helena!

HELENA—Gheid Storm.

STORM—I have a son; I don't know why I should tell you about him, perhaps because I want to prove that I have lived, and perhaps not. My son is a child, I am a man of few years and my son is like what I was at his age. He is thin, I was thin; he is quiet, I was quiet; he has delicate flesh, and I had also—well, then his mother died—

HELENA—The saddle comes down from the horse.

STORM—Well, she died—

HELENA—And that's over.

STORM—Well, there it is, I have a son—

HELENA—And that's not over. Do you resent that?

STORM—I don't know, perhaps. Sometimes I say to myself when I'm sitting by the fire alone—"You should have something to think of while sitting here—"

HELENA—In other words, you're living for the sake of your fire.

STORM—[*To himself.*] Some day I shall be glad I knew you.

HELENA—You go rather fast.

STORM—Yes, I shall have you to think of.

HELENA—When the fire is hot, you'll be glad to think of me?

STORM—Yes, all of us like to have a few things to tell to our children, and I have always shown all that's in my heart to my son.

HELENA—How horrible!

STORM—[*Startled.*] Why?

HELENA—Would you show everything that made your heart?

STORM—I believe in frankness—

HELENA—[*With something like anger.*] Well, some day your son will blow his head off, to be rid of frankness, before his skin is tough.

STORM—You are not making anything easier.

HELENA—I've never been callous enough to make things easier.

STORM—You're a queer woman—

HELENA—Yes, that does describe me.

STORM—[*Taking his leg off the table.*] Do you really want to know why I came? Because I need you—

HELENA—I'm not interested in corruption for the many.

STORM—[*Starting as if he had been struck.*] By God!

HELENA—Nor in misplaced satisfactions—

STORM—By God, what a woman!

HELENA—Nor do I participate in liberations—

STORM—[*In a low voice.*] I could hate you!

HELENA—I limit no man, feel what you can.

STORM—[*Taking a step toward her, the dog lifts its head.*] If it were not for those damned dogs of yours—I'd—I'd—

HELENA—Aristocracy of movement never made a dog bite—

STORM—That's a—strange thing to say—just at this moment.

HELENA—Not for me.

STORM—[*Sulky.*] Well, anyway, a cat may look at a King—

HELENA—Oh no, a cat may only look at what it sees.

STORM—Helena Hucksteppe.

HELENA—Yes.

STORM—I'm—attracted—to you.

HELENA—A magnet does not attract shavings.

STORM—[*With positive conviction.*] I *could* hate you.

HELENA—I choose my enemies.

STORM—[*Without warning, seizing her.*] By God, at least I can kiss you! [*He kisses her full on the mouth—she makes no resistance.*]

HELENA—[*In a calm voice.*] And this, I suppose, is what you call the "great moment of human contact."

STORM—[*Dropping his arms—turning pale.*] What are you trying to do to me?

HELENA—I'm doing it.

STORM—[*To himself.*] Yet it was you that I wanted—

HELENA—Mongrels may not dig up buried treasure.

STORM—[*In a sudden rage.*] You can bury your past as deep as you like, but carrion will out!

HELENA—[*Softly.*] And this is love.

STORM—[*His head in his arms.*] Oh, God, God!

HELENA—And you who like the taste of new things, come to me?

STORM—[*In a lost voice.*] Shall I have no joy?

HELENA—Joy? Oh, yes, of a kind.

STORM—And you—are angry with me?

HELENA—In the study of science, is the scientist angry when the fly possesses no amusing phenomena?

STORM—I wanted—to know—you—

HELENA—I am conscious of your failure.

STORM—I wanted something—some sign—

HELENA—Must I, who have spent my whole life in being myself, go out of my way to change some look in you?

STORM—That's why you are so terrible, you have spent all your life on yourself.

HELENA—Yes, men do resent that in women.

STORM—Yes, I suppose so. [*Pause.*] I should have liked to talk of—myself—

HELENA—You see I could not listen.

STORM—You are—intolerant.

HELENA—No—occupied—

STORM—You are probably—playing a game.

HELENA—[*With a gracious smile.*] You will get some personal good out of it, won't you?

STORM—I'm uncomfortable—

HELENA—Uncomfortable!

STORM—[*Beginning to be really uncomfortable.*] Who *are* you?

HELENA—I am a woman, Gheid Storm, who is *not* in need.

STORM—You're horrible!

HELENA—Yes, that too.

STORM—But somewhere you're vulnerable.

HELENA—Perhaps.

STORM—Only I don't quite know the spot.

HELENA—Spot?

STORM—Something, somewhere, hidden—

HELENA—Hidden! [*She laughs.*] *All* of me is vulnerable.

STORM—[*Setting his teeth.*] You tempt me.

HELENA—[*Wearily.*] It's not that kind.

STORM—I've lain awake thinking of you—many nights.

HELENA—That is too bad.

STORM—What is too bad?

HELENA—That you have had—fancies.

STORM—Why?

HELENA—Theft of much, makes much to return—

STORM—The world allows a man his own thoughts.

HELENA—Oh, no—

STORM—At least my thoughts are my own.

HELENA—Not one, so far.

STORM—What does that mean?

HELENA—You'll know when you try to think them again.

STORM—You mean I'm not making headway—well, you're right, I'm not—

HELENA—Now tell me what brought you through the window.

STORM—[Relieved.] I'm glad you ask that, it's the first human thing that's happened this afternoon.

HELENA—You have forgotten our great moment of human contact.

STORM—[Nervously.] Well—

HELENA—You were about to tell me what brought you?

STORM—I don't know—something no one speaks of—some great ease in your back—the look of a great lover—

HELENA—So—you scented a great lover—

STORM—I am a man—and I love—

HELENA—What have you done for love, Gheid Storm?

STORM—I've—never gone to the dogs—

HELENA—So?

STORM—I've always respected women.

HELENA—In other words: taken the coals out of the fire with the poker—continue—

STORM—That's all.

HELENA—And you dared to come to me! [*Her entire manner has changed.*]

STORM—No matter what you've been—done—I love you.

HELENA—Do not come so near. Only those who have helped to make such death as mine may go a little way toward the ardours of that decay.

STORM—What have I done?

HELENA—You have dared to bring to a woman, who has known love, the whinny of a pauper.

STORM—What am I?

HELENA—[*Softly, to herself.*] How sensitively the handles cling to the vase, how delicate is the flesh between the fingers.

STORM—I—I don't know you.

HELENA—[*Dropping her hands to her sides.*] Come here, Gheid Storm—[*Gheid approaches slowly, like a sleep walker*]. Put your hand on me. [*He does so as if in a dream.*] So! [*She looks first at his hand, then into his face, making it quite plain that he does not even know how to touch a woman.*] Yet you would be my lover, knowing not one touch that is mine, nor one word that is mine. My house is for men who have done their stumbling.

STORM—[*In an inaudible voice.*] I am going now—

HELENA—I cannot touch new things, nor see beginnings.

STORM—Helena! Helena!

HELENA—Do not call my name. There are too many names that must be called before mine.

STORM—Shall I die, and never have known you?

HELENA—Death, for you, will begin where my cradle started rocking—

STORM—Shall I have no love like yours?

HELENA—When I am an old woman, thinking of other things, you will, perhaps, be kissing a woman like me—

STORM—[*Moving blindly toward the door.*] Now I am going.

HELENA—[*In a quiet, level voice.*] The fall is almost here.

STORM—Yes, it's almost here.

HELENA—The leaves on the mountain road are turning yellow.

STORM—Yes, the leaves are turning.

HELENA—It's late, your son will be waiting dinner for you.

STORM—Don't take everything away.

HELENA—You will not even recall having seen me.

STORM—Can memory be taken too?

HELENA—Only that memory that goes past recollection may be kept.

STORM—[*At the door.*] Good night—

HELENA—[*Smiling.*] There is the window.

STORM—I could not lift my legs now.

HELENA—That's a memory you may keep.

STORM—Good night.

HELENA—Good-bye, Gheid Storm, and as you go down the hill, will you lock the gate, a dog thief passed in the night, taking my terrier with him.

STORM—The one with the brown spots?

HELENA—Yes.

STORM—That was a fine dog.

HELENA—Yes, she was a fine dog—restless.

STORM—They say any dog will follow any man who carries aniseed.

HELENA—Well, soon I return to the city.

STORM—You look tired.

HELENA—Yes, I am tired.

[*Gheid exits. Helena takes her old position, her back almost square to the audience.*]

CURTAIN

BEYOND THE END

———

Behind two spanking horses, in the heat of noon, rode Julie Ans-pacher. The air was full of the sound of windlasses and well water, where, from cool abysses, heavy buckets arose; and, too, the air was full of the perfect odour of small flowers. And Julie turned her head, gazing at the familiar line of road that ran away into the still more familiar distance.

The driver, a Scandinavian, who remembered one folk-tale in-volving a partridge and one popular song involving a woman, sat stiffly on his box holding the reins gently over the shining and sleek backs of the two mares.

He began to whistle the popular song now, swinging a little on his sturdy base, and drifting back with his tune came the tang of horse skin, wet beneath tight leather.

The horses were taking the hill, straining and moving their ears, and reaching the top, bounded forward in a whirl of dust. Still sitting rigid, the driver clucked, snapping his whip, and began talking in a dry deep bass.

"It's some time since we have seen you, Mrs. Anspacher."

Julie raised her thin long face from her collar and nodded.

"Yes," she answered in a short voice, and frowned.

"Your husband has gathered in the corn already, and the or-chards are hanging heavy."

"Are they?" she said, and tried to remember how many trees there were of apple and of pear.

The driver took in another foot of reins, and turning slightly around, so that he could look at her, said:

"It's good to see you again, Mrs. Anspacher."

She began to laugh. "Is it?" then with deliberation checked herself, and fixed her angry eyes straight ahead of her.

The child, loose-limbed with excessive youth, who sat at her side, lifted a small sharp face on which an aquiline nose perched with comic boldness. She half held, half dropped an old-fashioned ermine muff, the tails of which stuck out in all directions. She looked unhappy and expectant.

"You remember Mrs. Berling?" he went on. "She is married again."

"Is she?"

"Yes, ma'am."

He began to tell her about the local office for outgoing mails, where a nephew of her husband, Paytor, had taken a job.

The child sat so still that it was painful and Julie Anspacher moved away, thinking aloud:

"All is corruption."

The child started, and looked quickly away, as children will at something that they expect but do not understand. The driver beat the horses, until long lines of heavy froth appeared at the edges of the harness.

"What did you say, ma'am?"

"Nothing—I said all is lost from the beginning—if we only saw it—always."

The child looked at her slowly, puzzled, and looked down.

"Ann," said Julie Anspacher, suddenly lifting the muff over her hands, "did you ever see two such big horses before?" The child turned its head with brightness, and bending down tried to see between the driver's arms. Then she smiled.

"Are they yours?" she whispered.

Julie Anspacher took in a deep breath, stretching the silk of her waist across her breasts. "No," she answered, "they are not mine, but we have two—bigger—blacker."

"Can I see them?"

"Oh, yes, you shall see them. Don't be ridiculous."

The child shrank back into herself, clutching nervously at her muff. Julie Anspacher returned to her reflections.

It was almost five years since she had been home. Five years before in just such an Autumn the doctors had given her six months to live. One lung gone and the other going. They called it sometimes the White Death, and, sometimes, the love disease. She coughed a little, remembering, and the child at her side coughed too in echo, and the driver, puckering his forehead, reflected that Mrs. Anspacher was not cured.

She was thirty-nine—she should have died at thirty-four. In those five years Paytor had seen her five times, coming in over fourteen hours of the rails at Christmas. He cursed the doctors, called them fools.

The house appeared dull white between the locust trees, and the smoke, the same lazy Autumn smoke, rose in a still column straight into the obliterating day.

The driver reined in the horses until their foaming jaws struck against their harness, and with a quick bound Julie Anspacher jumped the side of the cart, the short modish tails of her jacket dancing above her hips. She turned around and thrusting her black gloved hands under the child, lifted her out. A dog barked. She began walking the ascent toward the house.

A maid, in dust cap, put her head out of an upstairs window, clucked, drew it in and slammed the sash, and Paytor, with slow and deliberate steps, moved toward the figure of his wife and the child.

He was a man of middle height, with a close-cropped beard that ended in a grey wedge on his chin. He was sturdy, a strong man, almost too pompous, but with kindly blue eyes and a long thin mouth. As he walked he threw his knees out, which gave him a rocking though substantial gait. He was slightly surprised and raised the apricot-coloured veil that covered the keen newness of her face, and leaning down kissed her twice upon both cheeks.

"And where does the child come from?" he inquired, touching the little girl's chin.

"Come along, don't be ridiculous!" Julie said impatiently, and swept on toward the house.

He ran after her. "I'm glad to see you," he went on, warmly, trying to keep up with her rapid strides, that swung the child half off the ground, stumbling, trotting.

"Tell me what the doctors said—cured?"

There was a note of happiness in his voice. "Not that I really give a damn what they think, I always told you you would live to a ripe old age, as they say. What did they do to Marie Bashkirtseff? Locked her up in a dark room, shut all the windows—and of course she died—that was their method then—and now it's Koch's tuberculin—all nonsense."

"It worked well with some people," she said, going ahead of him into the living room. "There was one boy there—well—of that later. Will you have someone put Ann to bed—the trip was bad for her. See how sleepy the child is—run along, Ann," she added, pushing her slightly but kindly toward the maid. Then when they had disappeared, she stood looking about her, drawing off her gloves.

"I'm glad you took down the crystals—I always hated them."— She moved to the windows.

"I didn't, the roof fell in—just after my last visit in December. You're looking splendid, Julie." He coloured. "I'm glad, you know— awfully glad. I began to think—well, not that the doctors know anything," he said, laughing: "but it's a drop here of about fifteen hundred feet, but your heart is good—always was."

"What do you know about my heart, Paytor?" Julie said, angrily. "You don't know what you are talking about at all. The child—"

"Well, yes—?"

"Her name is Ann," she finished sulkily.

"It's a sweet name—it was your mother's, too. Whose is she?"

"Oh, good heavens!" Julie cried, moving around the room. "Mine, mine, mine, of course, whose would she be if not mine?"

He looked at her. "Yours—why, Julie—how absurd!" Slowly the colour left his face.

"I know—we have got to talk it over—it's all got to be arranged, it's terrible. But she is nice, a bright child, a good child."

"What in the world is all this about?" he demanded, stopping in front of her. "What are you in this mood for—what have I done?"

"Good heavens! What have you done? What a ridiculous man you are. Why nothing, of course, absolutely nothing!" She waved her arm. "That's not it—why do you bring yourself in? I'm not blaming you, I'm not asking to be forgiven. I've been down on my knees, I've beaten my head on the ground, abased myself, but," she said in a terrible voice, "it is not low enough, the ground is not low enough, to bend is not enough; to ask forgiveness is not enough, to receive it is nothing. There isn't the right kind of misery in the world for me to suffer, nor the right kind of pity for you to feel, there isn't the right word in the world to heal me up. It's good to forgive, to be forgiven, but that's for ordinary things. This is beyond that—it's something you can experience but never feel—there are not enough nerves, blood cells, flesh—to feel it. You suffer insufficiently; it's like drinking insufficiently, sleeping insufficiently. I'm not asking anything because there is nothing that I can receive—how primitive to be able to receive—"

"But, Julie—"

"It's not that," she said roughly, tears swimming in her eyes. "Of course I love you. But think of it, a danger to everyone excepting those like yourself. Curious, involved in a problem affecting only a small per cent of humanity, sick, frightened, filled with fever and lust perhaps—with nothing, nothing coming after, whatever you do, but death—then you go on—it goes on—then the child—and life probably, for a time."

"Well—"

"I couldn't tell you. I thought, 'Well, I'll die next month,' and finally I didn't want to go off—although I did, you know what I mean. Then her father died—they say her lungs are weak—death, death perpetuating itself, that's funny you see—and the doctors—" She swung around: "You're right—they lied, and I lived through—all the way—all the way!"

He turned his face from her.

"The real thing," she went on in a pained voice, "is to turn our torment toward the perfect design. I didn't want to go beyond you —that was not my purpose. I thought there was not to be any more me. I wanted to leave nothing behind but you, only you. You must believe this or I can't bear it—and still," she continued, walking around the room impatiently, "there was a somehow hysterical joy in it too. I thought, if you had real perception, that 'something' that we must possess, that must be at the bottom of us somewhere—or there wouldn't be such an almost sensuous desire for it, that 'something' that, at times, is so near us that it becomes obscene, well, I thought, if Paytor has this—and mind you, I knew all the time that you didn't have it—that you would understand. And when you had been gone a long time I said, 'Paytor understands'—and I would say to myself—'Now, at this moment—at ten-thirty precisely, if I could be with Paytor he would say "I see,"' but so soon as I had the time table in my hand I knew that there was no such feeling in your bosom—nothing at all."

"Don't you feel horror?" he asked in a loud voice, suddenly.

"No, I don't feel horror—horror is conflict—and I have none— I'm alien to life."

"Have you a religion, Julie?" he asked, still in the same loud voice, as if he were addressing someone a little raised, yet invisible, as one tries to see a choir.

"I don't know—I don't think so. I've tried to believe in something external, something that might envelop this and carry it beyond—that's what we demand of our faiths, isn't it? But I always return to a fixed notion that there is something more fitting than a possible release."

He put his hands to his head. "You know," he said, "I've always thought that a woman, because she can have children, ought to know the truth—the very fact that she can do something so really preposterous ought to make her equally capable of the other preposterous thing—well—"

She coughed, her handkerchief before her face—she laughed with brightness. "One learns to be careful about death—but never, never about—" She didn't finish but stared before her.

"Why did you bring the child here—why did you return at all then—after so long a time—it seems all so mixed up?"

"I don't know—Perhaps because there is a right and a wrong, and a good and an evil. I had to find out—and if there's such a thing as everlasting mercy—I want to find out about that also—there's a flavour of unfamiliar intimacy about it all, though, this Christian treatment—" She had a way of lifting up the side of her face, closing her eyes. "I thought—Paytor may know."

"Know what?"

"Will know—well, will be able to divide me against myself—Personally I don't feel divided—I seem to be a sane and balanced whole—a hopelessly mixed, but perfect design. So I said Paytor will be able to see where this divides and departs. Though all the time I never for a moment felt that there was a system working on a this for that basis, but that there was only this *and* that—in other words—I wanted to be set wrong. . .You understand?"

"And you yourself," he inquired, in the same loud voice, "cannot feel the war? Well, then, what about me?—you must realize what you have done—turned everything upside down—oh, I won't even say betrayed me—it's much less than that, what most of us do, we betray circumstances—well, I can't do anything for you," he said sharply. "I can't do anything at all—I'm sorry, I'm very sorry—but there it is"—he began to grimace and twitch his shoulders.

"The child has it too," Julie Anspacher said, looking up at him. "I shall die soon.—It's ridiculous," she added, with the tears streaming down her face. "You are strong, always were—and so were all your family before you—not one of them in their graves under ninety—it's all wrong—it's quite ridiculous."

"I don't know. Perhaps it's not ridiculous. One must be very careful not to come, too hastily, to a conclusion." He began searching for his pipe.

"Only you know yourself, Julie, how I torment myself, if it's a big enough thing, for days, weeks, years; and the reason is, the real reason is, that I come to my conclusions instantly, and then fight to destroy them." He seemed to Julie a little pompous now. "It's because first I'm human, and second, logical. Well, I don't know—perhaps I'll be able to tell you something later—give you a beginning at least—later—" He twitched his shoulders and went out, closing the door after him. She heard him climbing the familiar creaking stairs, the yellow painted stairs that led up into the roof—she heard him strike a match—then silence.

The dark had begun, closing in about bushes and barn, and filling the air with moist joyousness, the joyousness of autumn that trusts itself to the darkness, and Julie leaned on her hand by the shelf and listened.

She could hear, far away and faint, the sound of dogs on heavy chains. She tried to stop, listening to the outside, but her thoughts rotted away like clouds in a wind.

The sense of tears came to her, but it was only a sentimental memory of her early childhood, and it brought a smile to her long face. She had cried once when they made her kiss a dead priest—"Qui habitare facit sterilem—matrem filiorum laetantem"—then "Gloria Patri—" and she had wept then, or thought she had, because he was not only beyond glory and all mercy, but beyond the dubious comfort of the feeling.

She heard Paytor walking above, and the smoke of his pipe crept down between loose boards and uneven plaster and laths.

She went—quite mechanically—over to a chest in one corner, and opened the lid. A shirt waist, of striped taffeta, one she had worn years before, some old Spanish lace—her mother's—the child—

Paytor did not seem to like the child—"How ridiculous!" she thought. "She is good, quiet, gentle—but that's not enough now." She removed her hat. Living with Paytor and the child—Paytor so strong,—always was, and so was his family—and she sickly, coughing. Perhaps she had made a mistake in coming back. She went toward the steps to tell this to Paytor but thought better of it. That wasn't what she wanted to say.

The hours drew out and Julie Anspacher, sitting now at the window overlooking the garden—nodded without sleep—long dreams—grotesque and abominable—stupid irrelevances dull and interminable. Somewhere little Ann coughed in her sleep. Julie

Anspacher coughed also, and in between, the sound of Paytor walking up and down, and the smell of tobacco growing stronger.

To take her own life, that was right, if only she had not the habit of fighting death—"but death is past knowing, and to know is better than to make right—" She shook her head. "That's another detour on the wrong side," she told herself. "If only I had the power to feel pain as unbearable, a gust of passion, of impatience, and all would be over—but I've stood so much so long, there is no too long." She thought what she would not give for any kind of feeling, anything that was vital and sudden and determining. "If Paytor will have patience I will get around to it."

Then it seemed that something must happen, must inevitably happen.

"If I could only think of the right word before it happens," she said to herself, over and over, and over. "It's because I'm cold and I can't think, I'll think soon—" She would take her jacket off, put on her coat—

She got up, running her hand along the wall. Or had she left it on the chair? "I can't think of the word," she said to keep her mind on something.

She turned around. All his family—long lives. "And me too, me too," she murmured. She became dizzy. "It is because I must get on my knees—but it isn't low enough." She contradicted herself. "Yet if I put my head down—way down—down—"

Then she heard the shot. "He has quick warm blood" went through her mind—and her blood was cold.

Her forehead had not quite touched the boards, now she touched them, but she got up immediately, stumbling over her dress.

PASTORAL

———

A frog leaps out across the lawn,
And crouches there—all heavy and alone,
And like a blossom, pale and over-blown,
Once more the moon turns dim against the dawn.

Crawling across the straggling panoply
Of little roses, only half in bloom,
It strides within that beamed and lofty room
Where an ebon stallion looms upon the hay.

The stillness moves, and seems to grow immense,
A shuddering dog starts, dragging at its chain,
Thin, dusty rats slink down within the grain,
And in the vale the first far bells commence.

Here in the dawn, with mournful doomèd eyes
A cow uprises, moving out to bear
A soft-lipped calf with swarthy birth-swirled hair,
And wide wet mouth, and droll uncertainties.

The grey fowls fight for places in the sun,
The mushrooms flare, and pass like painted fans:
All the world is patient in its plans—
The seasons move forever, one on one.

Small birds lie sprawling vaguely in the heat,
And wanly pluck at shadows on their breasts,

And where the heavy grape-vine leans and rests,
White butterflies lift up their furry feet.

The wheat grows querulous with unseen cats;
A fox strides out in anger through the corn,
Bidding each acre wake and rise to mourn
Beneath its sharps and through its throaty flats.

And so it is, and will be year on year,
Time in and out of date, and still on time
A billion grapes plunge bleeding into wine
And bursting, fall like music on the ear.

The snail that marks the girth of night with slime,
The lonely adder hissing in the fern,
The lizard with its ochre eyes aburn—
Each is before, and each behind its time.

OSCAR

Before the house rose two stately pine trees, and all about small firs and hemlocks. The garden path struggled up to the porch between wildflowers and weeds, and looming against its ancient bulk the shadows of out-houses and barns.

It stood among the hills, and just below around a curve in the road, lay the placid grey reservoir.

Sometimes parties would cross the fields, walking slowly toward the mountains. And sometimes children could be heard murmuring in the underbrush of things they scarcely knew.

Strange things had happened in this country town. Murder, theft, and little girls found weeping, and silent morose boys scowling along in the ragweed, with half-shut sunburned eyelids.

The place was wild, deserted and impossible in Winter. In Summer it was over-run with artists and town folk with wives and babies. Every Saturday there were fairs on the green, where second-hand articles were sold for a song, and flirting was formidable and passing. There were picnics, mountain climbings, speeches in the town-hall, on the mark of the beast, on sin, and democracy, and once in a while a lecture on something that "everyone should know," attended by mothers, their offspring left with servants who knew what everyone shouldn't.

Then there were movies, bare legs, deacons, misses in cascades of curls and on Sunday one could listen to Mr. Widdie, the clergyman, who suffered from consumption, speak on love of one's neighbour.

In this house and in this town had lived, for some fifteen years or so, Emma Gonsberg.

She was a little creature, lively, smiling, extremely good-natured. She had been married twice, divorced once, and was now a widow still in her thirties.

Of her two husbands she seldom said anything. Once she made the remark: "Only fancy, they never did catch on to me at all."

She tried to be fashionable, did her hair in the Venetian style, wore gowns after the manner of Lady de Bath entering her carriage; and tried to cultivate only those who could tell her "where she stood."

Her son Oscar was fourteen or thereabouts. He wore distinctly over-decorative English clothes, and remembered two words of some obscure Indian dialect that seemed to mean "fleas," for whenever he flung these words defiantly at visitors they would go off into peals of laughter, headed by his mother. At such times he would lower his eyes and show a row of too heavy teeth.

Emma Gonsberg loved flowers, but could not grow them. She admired cats because there was "nothing servile about them," but they would not stay with her; and though she loved horses and longed to be one of those daring women who could handle them "without being crushed in the stalls," they nevertheless ignored her with calm indifference. Of her loves, passions and efforts, she had managed to raise a few ill-smelling pheasants, and had to let it go at that.

In the Winter she led a lonely and discriminating life. In the Summer her house filled with mixed characters, as one might say. A hot melancholy Jew, an officer who was always upon the point of depreciating his medals in a conceited voice, and one other who swore inoffensively.

Finally she had given this sort of thing up, partly because she had managed, soon after, to get herself entangled with a man called Ulric Straussmann. A tall rough fellow, who said he came from the Tyrol; a fellow without sensibilities but with a certain bitter sensuality. A good-natured creature as far as he went, with vivid streaks of German lust, which had at once something sentimental and something careless about it; the type who can turn the country, with a single gesture, into a brothel, and makes of children strong enemies. He showed no little audacity in putting things into people's minds that he would not do himself.

He smelled very strongly of horses, and was proud of it. He pretended a fondness for all that goes under hide or hair, but a collie bitch, known for her gentleness, snapped at him and bit him. He invariably carried a leather thong, braided at the base for a handle, and would stand for hours talking, with his legs apart, whirling this contrived whip, and, looking out of the corner of his eyes would pull his moustache, waiting to see which of the ladies would draw her feet in.

He talked in a rather even, slightly nasal tone, wetting his lips with a long outthrust of tongue, like an animal. His teeth were splendid and his tongue unusually red, and he prided himself on these and on the calves of his legs. They were large, muscular and rather handsome.

He liked to boast that there was nothing that he could not do and be forgiven, because, as he expressed it, "I have always left people satisfied." If it were hate or if it were love, he seemed to have come off with unusual success. "Most people are puny," he would add, "while I am large, strong, healthy. Solid flesh through and through," whereat he would pound his chest and smile.

He was new to the town and sufficiently insolent to attract attention. There was also something childishly naïve in him, as there is in all tall and robust men who talk about themselves. This probably saved him, because when he was drinking he often became gross and insulting, but he soon put the women of the party in a good humour by giving one of them a hearty and good-natured slap on the rear that she was not likely to forget.

Besides this man Emma had a few old friends of the less interesting, though better-read, type. Among them, however, was an exception, Oliver Kahn, a married man with several children one heard of and never saw. A strange, quiet man who was always talking. He had splendid eyes and a poor mouth—very full lips. In the beginning one surmised that he had been quite an adventurer.

He had an odour about him of the rather recent cult of the "terribly good." He seemed to have been unkind to his family in some way, and was spending the rest of his life in a passion of regret and remorse. He had become one of those guests who are only missed when absent. He finally stayed for good, sleeping in an ante-room with his boots on,—his one royal habit.

In the beginning Emma had liked him tremendously. He was at once gentle and furious, but of late, just prior to the Straussmann affair, he had begun to irritate her. She thought to herself, "He is going mad, that's all." She was angry at herself for saying "that's all," as if she had expected something different, more momentous.

He had enormous appetites, he ate like a Porthos and drank like a Pantagruel, and talked hour after hour about the same thing, "Love of one's neighbour," and spent his spare time in standing with his hands behind him, in front of the pheasants' cage. He had been a snipe hunter in his time, and once went on a big game hunt, but now he said he saw something more significant here.

He had, like all good sportsmen, even shot himself through the hand, but of late he pretended that he did not remember what the scar came from.

He seemed to suffer a good deal. Evil went deep and good went deep and he suffered the tortures of the damned. He wept and laughed and ate and drank and slept, and year by year his eyes grew sweeter, tenderer, and his mouth fuller, more gross.

The child Oscar did not like Kahn, yet sometimes he would become extraordinarily excited, talk very fast, almost banteringly, a little malignly, and once when Kahn had taken his hand he drew it away angrily. "Don't," he said.

"Why not?"

"Because it is dirty," he retorted maliciously.

"As if you really knew of what I was thinking," Kahn said, and put his own hands behind him.

Emma liked Kahn, was attached to him. He mentioned her faults without regret or reproval, and this in itself was a divine sort of love.

He would remark: "We cannot be just because we are bewildered; we ought to be proud enough to welcome our enemies as judges, but we hate, and to hate is the act of the incurious. I love with an everlasting but a changing love, because I know I am the wrong sort of man to be good—and because I revere the shadow on the threshold."

"What shadow, Kahn?"

"In one man we called it Christ—it is energy; for most of us it is dead, a phantom. If you have it you *are* Christ, and if you have only a little of it you are but the promise of the Messiah."

These seemed great words, and she looked at him with a little admiring smile.

"You make me uneasy for fear that I have not said 'I love you with an everlasting love,' often enough to make it an act of fanaticism."

As for Oscar, he did what he liked, which gave him character, but made him difficult to live with.

He was not one of those "weedy" youths, long of leg, and stringy like "jerked beef, thank God!" as his mother said to visitors. He was rather too full-grown, thick of calf and hip and rather heavy of feature. His hands and feet were not out of proportion as is usually the case with children of his age, but they were too old looking.

He did not smoke surreptitiously. On the contrary he had taken out a pipe one day in front of his mother, and filling it, smoked in silence, not even with a frightened air, and for that matter not even with a particularly bold air;—he did it quite simply, as something he had finally decided to do, and Emma Gonsberg had gone off to Kahn with it, in a rather helpless manner.

Most children swing in circles about a room, clumsily. Oscar on the contrary walked into the four corners placidly and officially, looked at the backs of the books here and a picture there, and even grunted approvingly at one or two in quite a mature manner.

He had a sweetheart, and about her and his treatment of her there were only a few of the usual signs—he was shy, and passionately immersed in her, there was little of the casual smartness of first calf love about it, though he did in truth wave her off with a grin if he was questioned.

He took himself with seriousness amounting to a lack of humour—and though he himself knew that he was a youth, and had the earmarks of adolescence about him—and know it he certainly did—once he said, "Well, what of it—is that any reason why I should not be serious about everything?" This remark had so astonished his mother that she had immediately sent for Kahn to know if he thought the child was precocious—and Kahn had answered, "If he were, I should be better pleased."

"But what is one to expect?"

"Children," he answered, "are never what they are supposed to be, and they never have been. He may be old for his age, but what child hasn't been?"

In the meantime, she tried to bring Straussmann and Kahn together—"My house is all at odds," she thought, but these two never hit it off. Straussmann always appeared dreadfully superficial and cynical, and Kahn dull and good about nothing.

"They have both got abnormal appetites," she thought wearily. She listened to them trying to talk together of an evening on the piazza steps. Kahn was saying:

"You must, however, warn yourself, in fact I might say arm yourself, against any sensation of pleasure in doing good; this is very difficult, I know, but it can be attained. You can give and forgive and tolerate gently and, as one might say, casually, until it's a second nature."

"There you have it, tolerate—who wants tolerance, or a second nature? Well, let us drop it. I feel like a child—it's difficult not to feel like a child."

"Like Oscar—he has transports—even at his age," Emma added hesitatingly. "Perhaps that's not quite as it should be?"

"The memory of growing up is worse than the fear of death," Kahn remarked, and Emma sighed.

"I don't know; the country was made for children, they say—I could tell you a story about that," Straussmann broke off, whistling to Oscar. "Shall I tell Oscar about the country—and what it is really like?" he asked Emma, turning his head.

"Let the boy alone."

"Why, over there in that small village," Straussmann went on, taking Oscar by the arm. "It is a pretty tale I could tell you—perhaps I will when you are older—but don't let your mother persuade you that the country is a nice, healthful, clean place, because, my child, it's corrupt."

"Will you let the boy alone!" Emma cried, turning very red.

"Ah, eh—I'll let him alone right enough—but it won't make much difference—you'll see," he went on. "There is a great deal told to children that they should not hear, I'll admit, but there wasn't a thing I didn't know when I was ten. It happened one day in a hotel in Southampton—a dark place, gloomy, smelling frightfully of mildew, the walls were damp and stained. A strange place, eh, to learn the delights of love, but then our parents seldom dwell on the delights,—they are too taken up with the sordid details, the mere sordid details. My father had a great beard, and I remember thinking that it would have been better if he hadn't said such things. I wasn't much good afterwards for five or six years, but my sister was different. She enjoyed it immensely and forgot all about it almost immediately, excepting when I reminded her."

"Go to bed, Oscar," Emma said abruptly.

He went, and on going up the steps he did not let his fingers trail along the spindles of the banisters with his usual "Eeny meeny miny mo," etc.

Emma was a little troubled and watched him going up silently, hardly moving his arms.

"Children should be treated very carefully, they should know as much as possible, but in a less superficial form than they must know later."

"I think a child is born corrupt and attains to decency," Straussmann said grinning.

"If you please," Emma cried gaily, "we will talk about things we understand."

Kahn smiled. "It's beautiful, really beautiful," he said, meaning her gaiety. He always said complimentary things about her lightness of spirit, and always in an angry voice.

"Come, come, you are going mad. What's the good of that?" she said, abruptly, thinking, "He is a man who discovered himself once too often."

"You are wrong, Emma, I am not worthy of madness."

"Don't be on your guard, Kahn," she retorted.

Oscar appeared before her suddenly, barefoot. She stared at him. "What is it?" she at last managed to ask in a faint almost suffocated voice.

"I want to kiss you," he whispered.

She moved toward him slowly, when, half way, he hurried toward her, seized her hand, kissed it, and went back into the house.

"My God," she cried out. "He is beginning to think for himself," and ran in after him.

She remembered how she had talked to him the night before, only the night before. "You must love with an everlasting but a changing love," and he became restless. "With an everlasting but a changing love."

"What do you mean by 'changing'?" His palms were moist, and his feet twitched.

"A love that takes in every detail, every element—that can understand without hating, without distinction, I think."

"Why do you say, 'I think'?"

"I mean, I know," she answered, confused.

"Get that Kahn out, he's a rascal," he said, abruptly, grinning.

"What are you saying, Oscar?" she demanded, turning cold. "I'll never come to your bed again, take your hands and say 'Our Father.'"

"It will be all right if you send that man packing," he said, stressing the word "packing."

She was very angry, and half started toward the door. Then she turned back. "Why do you say that, Oscar?"

"Because he makes you nervous—well, then—because he crouches"; he saw by his mother's face that she was annoyed, puzzled, and he turned red to his ears. "I don't mean that, I mean he isn't good; he's just watching for something good to happen, to take place—" His voice trailed off, and he raised his eyes solemn and full of tears to her face. She leaned down and kissed him, tucking him in like a "little boy."

"But I'm not a little boy," he called out to her.

And tonight she did not come down until she thought Kahn and Straussmann had gone.

Kahn had disappeared, but Straussmann had taken a turn or two about the place and was standing in the shadow of the stoop when she came out.

"Come," he said. "What is it that you want?"

"I think it's religion," she answered abruptly. "But it's probably love."

"Let us take a walk," he suggested.

They turned in toward the shadows of the great still mountains and the denser, more arrogant shadows of the out-houses and barns. She looked away into the silence, and the night, and a warm sensation as of pleasure or of something expected but intangible came over her, and she wanted to laugh, to cry, and thinking of it she knew that it was neither.

She was almost unconscious of him for a little, thinking of her son. She raised her long silk skirts about her ankles and tramped off into the dampness. A whippoorwill was whistling off to the right. It sounded as if he were on the fence, and Emma stopped and tried to make it out. She took Ulric's arm presently, and feeling his muscles swell began to think of the Bible. "Those who take by the sword shall die by the sword. And those who live by the flesh shall die by the flesh."

She wished that she had someone she could believe in. She saw a door before her mental eye, and herself opening it and saying, "Now tell me this, and what it means,—only today I was thinking 'those who live by the flesh'"—and as suddenly the door was slammed in her face. She started back.

"You are nervous," he said in a pleased whisper.

Heavy stagnant shadows sprawled in the path. "So many million leaves and twigs to make one dark shadow," she said, and was sorry because it sounded childishly romantic, quite different from what she had intended, what she had meant.

They turned the corner of the carriage-house. Something moved, a toad, grey and ugly, bounced across her feet and into the darkness of the hedges. Coming to the entrance of the barn they paused. They could distinguish sleeping hens, the white films moving on their eyes—and through a window at the back, steam rising from the dung heap.

"There don't seem to be any real farmers left," she said aloud, thinking of some book she had read about the troubles of the peasants and landholders.

"You're thinking of my country," he said smiling.

"No, I wasn't," she said. "I was wondering what it is about the country that makes it seem so terrible?"

"It's your being a Puritan—a tight-laced delightful little Puritan."

She winced at the words, and decided to remain silent.

It was true, Straussmann was in a fever of excitement—he was always this way with women, especially with Emma. He tried to conceal it for the time being, thinking, rightly, that a display of it would not please her just at the moment—"but it would be only a matter of minutes when she would welcome it," he promised himself, and waited.

He reflected that she would laugh at him. "But she would enjoy it just the same. The way with all women who have had anything to do with more than one man and are not yet forty," he reflected. "They like what they get, but they laugh at you, and know you are lying—"

"Oh, my God!" Emma said suddenly, drawing her arm away and wiping her face with her handkerchief.

"What's the matter?"

"Nothing, it's the heat."

"It is warm," he said dismally.

"I despise everything, I really despise everything, but you won't believe—I mean everything when I say everything—you'll think I mean some one thing—won't you?" she went on hurriedly. She felt that she was becoming hysterical.

"It doesn't matter," he rejoined, walking on beside her, his heart beating violently. "Down, you dog," he said aloud.

"What is that?" She raised her eyes and he looked into them, and they both smiled.

"That's better. I wish I were God."

"A desire for a vocation."

"Not true, and horrid, as usual," she answered, and she was hot and angry all at once.

He pulled at his moustache and sniffed. "I can smell the hedges— ah, the country is a gay deceiver—it smells pleasant enough, but it's treacherous. The country, my dear Emma, has done more to cor- rupt man, to drag him down, to turn him loose upon his lower instincts, than morphine, alcohol and women. That's why I like it, that's why it's the perfect place for women. They are devils and should be driven out, and as there's more room in the country and consequently less likelihood of driving them out in too much of a hurry, there is more time for amusement." He watched her out of the corner of his eye as he said these things to note if they were ill advised. They seemed to leave her cold, but tense.

A little later they passed the barns again.

"What was that?" Emma asked suddenly.

"I heard nothing."

But she had heard something, and her heart beat fearfully. She recognized Oscar's voice. She reached up signing Straussmann to be quiet. She did not want him to hear; she wished that the ground would yawn, would swallow him up.

"See that yellow flower down there," she said, pointing toward the end of the path they had just come. "I want it, I must have it, please." He did as he was bid, amiably enough.

She listened—she heard the voice of Oscar's little sweetheart:

"It seems as if we were one already". . . It was high, resolute, unflagging, without emotion, a childish parroting of some novel. Oscar's voice came back, half smothered:

"Do you really care—more than you like Berkeley?"

"Yes, I do," she answered in the same false treble, "lots more."

"Come here," he said softly—the hay rustled.

"I don't want to—the rye gets into my hair and spoils it."

"Dolly, do you like the country?"

"Yes, I do,"—without conviction.

"We will go to the city," he answered.

"Oh, Oscar, you're so strong," she giggled, and it sent a cold shudder through Emma's being.

Then presently, "What's the matter, Oscar—why, you're crying."

"I'm not—well, then yes, I am—what of it?—you'll understand, too, some day."

She was evidently frightened, because she said in a somewhat loosened key, "No one would ever believe that we were as much in love as we are, would they, Oscar?"

"No, why do you ask that?"

"It's a great pity," she said again with the false sound, and sighed.

"Do you care? Why do you care?"

Straussmann was coming back with the yellow flower between thumb and forefinger. Emma ran a little way to meet him.

"Come, let us go home the other way."

"Rather, let us not go home," he said, boldly, and took her wrist, hurting her.

"Ah," she said. "Vous m'avez blessée d'amour"—ironically.

"Yes, speak French, it helps women like you at such moments," he said, brutally, and kissed her.

But kissing him back, she thought, "The fool, why does Oscar take her so seriously when they are both children, and she is torturing him."

"My love, my sweet, my little love," he was babbling.

She tried to quench this, trembling a little. "But tell me, my friend—no, not so hasty—what do you think of immortality?" He had pushed her so far back that there was no regaining her composure. "My God, in other words, what of the will to retribution!"

But she could not go on. "I've tried to," she thought.

Later, when the dawn was almost upon them, he said: "How sad to be drunk, only to die. For the end of all man is Fate, in other words, the end of all man is vulgar."

She felt the need of something that had not been.

"I'm not God, you see, after all."

"So I see, madam," he said. "But you're a damned clever little woman."

When she came in, she found Kahn lying flat on his back, his eyes wide open.

"Couldn't you sleep?"

"No, I could not sleep."

She was angry. "I'm sorry—you suffer."

"Yes, a little."

"Kahn," she cried in anguish, flinging herself on her knees beside him. "What should I have done, what shall I do?"

He put his hand on her cheek. "My dear, my dear," he said, and sighed. "I perhaps was wrong."

She listened.

"Very wrong, I see it all now; I am an evil man, an old and an evil being."

"No, no!"

"Yes, yes," he said gently, softly, contradicting her. "Yes, evil, and pitiful, and weak"; he seemed to be trying to remember something. "What is it that I have overlooked?" He asked the question in such a confused voice that she was startled.

"Is it hate?" she asked.

"I guess so, yes, I guess that's it."

"Kahn, try to think—there must be something else."

"Madness."

She began to shiver.

"Are you cold?"

"No, it's not cold."

"No, it's not cold," he repeated after her. "You are not cold, Emma, you are a child."

Tears began to roll down her cheeks.

"Yes," he continued sadly. "You too will hear: remorse is the medium through which the evil spirit takes possession."

And again he cried out in anguish. "But I'm *not* superficial—I may have been wanton, but I've not been superficial. I wanted to give up everything, to abandon myself to whatever IT demanded, to do whatever IT directed and willed. But the terrible thing is I don't know what abandon is. I don't know when it's abandon and when it's just a case of minor calculation.

"The real abandon is not to know whether one throws oneself off a cliff or not, and not to care. But I can't do it, because I must know, because I'm afraid if I did cast myself off, I should find that I had thrown myself off the lesser thing after all, and that," he said in a horrified voice, "I could never outlive, I could never have faith again. And so it is that I shall never know, Emma; only children and the naïve know, and I am too sophisticated to accomplish the divine descent."

"But you must tell me," she said, hurriedly. "What am I to do, what am I to think? My whole future depends on that, on your answer—on knowing whether I do an injustice not to hate, not to strike, not to kill—well, you must tell me—I swear it is my life— my entire life."

"Don't ask me, I can't know, I can't tell. I who could not lead one small sheep, what could I do with a soul, and what still more could I do with you? No," he continued, "I'm so incapable. I am so mystified. Death would be a release, but it wouldn't settle anything. It never settles anything, it simply wipes the slate, it's merely a way of putting the sum out of mind, yet I wish I might die. How do I know now but that everything I have thought, and said, and done, has not been false, a little abyss from which I shall crawl laughing at the evil of my own limitation."

"But the child—what have I been telling Oscar—to love with an everlasting love—"

"That's true," he said.

"Kahn, listen. What have I done to him, what have I done to myself? What are we all doing here—are we all mad—or are we merely excited—overwrought, hysterical? I must know, I must know." She took his hand and he felt her tears upon it.

"Kahn, is it an everlasting but a changing love—what kind of love is that?"

"Perhaps that's it," he cried, jumping up, and with a gesture tore his shirt open at the throat. "Look, I want you to see, I run upon the world with a bared breast—but never find the blade—ah, the civility of our own damnation—that's the horror. A few years ago, surely this could not have happened. Do you know," he said, turning his eyes all hot and burning upon her, "the most terrible thing in the world is to bare the breast and never to feel the blade enter!" He buried his face in his hands.

"But, Kahn, you must think, you must give me an answer. All this indecision is all very well for us, for all of us who are too old to change, for all of us who can reach God through some plaything we have used as a symbol, but there's my son, what is he to think, to feel, he has no jester's stick to shake, nor stool to stand on. Am I responsible for him? Why," she cried frantically, "must I be responsible for him? I tell you I won't be, I can't. I won't take it upon myself. But I have, I have. Is there something that can make me immune to my own blood? Tell me—I must wipe the slate—the fingers are driving me mad—can't he stand alone now? Oh, Kahn, Kahn!" she cried, kissing his hands. "See, I kiss your hands, I am doing so much. You must be the prophet—you can't do less for the sign I give you—I must know, I must receive an answer, I *will* receive it."

He shook her off suddenly, a look of fear came into his eyes.

"Are you trying to frighten me?" he whispered. She went into the hall, into the dark, and did not know why, or understand anything. Her mind was on fire, and it was consuming things that were strange and merciful and precious.

Finally she went into her son's room and stood before his bed. He lay with one feverish cheek against a dirty hand, his knees drawn up; his mouth had a peculiar look of surprise about it.

She bent down, called to him, not knowing what she was doing. "Wrong, wrong," she whispered, and she shook him by the shoulders. "Listen, Oscar, get up. Listen to me!"

He awoke and cried out as one of her tears, forgotten, cold, struck against his cheek. An ague shook his limbs. She brought her face close to his.

"Son, hate too, that is inevitable—irrevocable—"

He put out his two hands and pushed them against her breast and in a subdued voice said, "Go away, go away," and he looked as if he were about to cry, but he did not cry.

She turned and fled into the hall.

However, in the morning, at breakfast, there was nothing unusual about her, but a tired softness and yielding of spirit; and at dinner, which was always late, she felt only a weary indifference when she saw Straussmann coming up the walk. He had a red and white handkerchief about his throat, and she thought, "How comic he looks."

"Good evening," he said.

"Good evening," she answered, and a touch of her old gaiety came into her voice. Kahn was already seated, and now she motioned Straussmann to follow. She began slicing the cold potted beef and asked them about sugar in their tea, adding, "Oscar will be here soon." To Kahn she showed only a very little trace of coldness, of indecision.

"No," Straussmann said, still standing, legs apart: "If you'll excuse me, I'd like a word or two with Kahn." They stepped off the porch together.

"Kahn," he said, going directly to the point, "listen," he took hold of Kahn's coat by the lapel. "You have known Emma longer than I have, you've got to break it to her." He flourished a large key under Kahn's nose, as he spoke.

"I've got him locked up in the out-house safe enough for the present, but we must do something immediately."

"What's the matter?" A strange, pleasant but cold sweat broke out upon Kahn's forehead.

"I found Oscar sitting beside the body of his sweetheart, what's-her-name; he had cut her throat with a kitchen knife, yes, with a kitchen knife—he seemed calm, but he would say nothing. What shall we do?"

"They'll say he was a degenerate from the start—"

"Those who live by the flesh—eh?"

"No," Kahn said, in a confused voice, "that's not it."

They stood and stared at each other so long that presently Emma grew nervous and came down the garden path to hear what it was all about.

ANTIQUE

———

A lady in a cowl of lawn
With straight bound tabs and muted eyes,
And lips fair thin and deftly drawn
   And oddly wise.

A cameo, a ruff of lace,
A neck cut square with corners laid;
A thin Greek nose and near the face
   A polished braid.

Low, sideways looped, of amber stain
The pale ears caught within its snare.
A profile like a dagger lain
   Between the hair.

KATRINA SILVERSTAFF

———

"We have eaten a great deal, my friend, against the day of God."

She was a fine woman, hard, magnificent, cold, Russian, married to a Jew, a doctor on the East Side.

You know that kind of woman, pale, large, with a heavy oval face.

A woman of 'material'—a lasting personality, in other words, a 'fashionable' woman, a woman who, had she lived to the age of forty odd, would have sat for long fine hours by some window, overlooking some desolate park, thinking of a beautiful but lazy means to an end.

She always wore large and stylish hats, and beneath them her mouth took on a look of pain at once proud, aristocratic and lonely.

She had studied medicine—but medicine in the interest of animals; she was a good horse doctor—an excellent surgeon on the major injuries to birds and dogs.

In fact she and her husband had met in a medical college in Russia—she had been the only woman in the class, the only one of the lot of them who smiled in a strange, hurt and sarcastic way when dissecting.

The men treated her like one of them, that is, they had no cringing mannerliness about their approach, they lost no poise before her, and tried no tricks as one might say.

The Silverstaffs had come to America, they had settled on the East Side, among 'their own people' as he would say; she never said anything when he talked like this, she sat passive, her hands in her lap, but her nostrils quivered, and somewhere under the skin of her cheek something trembled.

Her husband was the typical Jewish intellectual, a man with stiff, short, greying hair, prominent intelligent and kindly eyes, rather short, rather round, always smelling of Greek salad and carbolic acid, and always intensely interested in new medical journals, theories, discoveries.

He was a little dusty, a little careless, a little timid, but always gentle.

They had been in America scarcely eight months before the first child was born, a girl, and then following on her heels a boy, and then no more children.

Katrina Silverstaff stopped having her children as abruptly as she had begun having them; something complicated had entered her mind, and where there are definite complications of the kind that she suffered, there are no more children.

"We have eaten a great deal, my friend, against the day of God," she had said that.

She had said that one night, sitting in the dusk of their office. There was something inexpressibly funny in their sitting together in this office, with its globe of the world, its lung charts, its weighing machine, its surgical chair, and its bowl of ineffectual goldfish. Something inexpressibly funny and inexpressibly fecund, a fecundity suppressed by coldness, and a terrible determination—more terrible in that her husband Otto felt nothing of it.

He was very fond of her, and had he been a little more sensitive he would have been very glad to be proud of her. She never became confidential with him, and he never tried to overstep this, partly because he was unaware of it, and partly because he felt little need of a closer companionship.

She was a fine woman, he knew that; he never thought to question anything she did, because it was little, nor what she said, because it was less; there was an economy about her existence that simply forbade questioning. He felt in some dim way, that to criticize at all would be to stop everything.

Their life was typical of the East Side doctor's life. Patients all day for him, and the children for her, with an occasional call from someone who had a sick bird. In the evening they would sit around a table with just sufficient food, with just sufficient silver and linen, and one luxury: Katrina's glass of white wine.

Or sometimes they would go out to dine, to some kosher place, where everyone was too friendly and too ugly and too warm, and here he would talk of the day's diseases while she listened to the music and tried not to hear what her daughter was crying for.

He had always been a 'liberal,' from the first turn of the cradle. In the freedom of the people, in the betterment of conditions, he took the interest a doctor takes in seeing a wound heal.

As for Katrina Silverstaff, she never said anything about it, he never knew what she really thought, if she thought at all; it did not seem necessary for her to do or say anything, she was fine as she was, where she was. On the other hand it never occurred to him that she would not hear, with calmness at least, his long dissertations on capital.

At the opening of this story, Katrina's daughter was a little girl of ten, who was devoted to dancing, and who lay awake at nights worrying about the shape of her legs, which had already begun to swell with a dancer's muscles.

The boy was nine, thin, and wore spectacles.

And of course what happened was quite unaccountable.

A man, calling himself Castillion Rodkin, passed through one Summer, selling Carlyle's "French Revolution." Among the houses where he had left a copy was the house of Otto Silverstaff.

Katrina had opened the door, the maid was down with the measles, and the doctor was busy with a patient, a Jew much revered for his poetry.

She never bought anything of peddlers, and she seldom said more than "No, thank you." In this case she neither said "Thank you," nor closed the door—instead she held it open, standing a little aside for him to pass, and, utterly astonished, he did pass, waiting behind her in the hall for orders.

"We will go into the study," she said, "my husband is busy."

"I was selling Bibles last year," he remarked, "but they do not go down in this section."

"Yes," she answered, "I see," and she moved before him into the heavy damp parlour which was never unshuttered and which was never used. She reached up and turned on one solitary electric light.

Castillion Rodkin might have been of any nationality in the world; this was partly from having travelled in all countries, and also from a fluid temperament—little was fixed or firm in him, a necessary quality in a salesman.

Castillion Rodkin was below medium height, thin and bearded with a pale, almost white growth of hair. He was peculiarly colourless, his eyes were only a shade darker than his temples, and very restless.

She said simply, "We must talk about religion."

And with an awkwardness unusual to him he asked "Why?"

"Because," she said in a strained voice, making a hurt gesture, "it is so far from me."

He did not know what to say, of course, and lifting one thin leg in its white trousers he placed it carefully over the other.

She was sitting opposite him, her head turned a little to one side, not looking at anything. "You see," she said presently, "I want religion to become out of the reach of the few."

"Become's a queer word," he said.

"It is the only word," she answered, and there was a slight irritation in her voice, "because it is so irrevocably for the many."

"Yes," he said mechanically, and reached up to his beard, leaving his hand there under a few strands of hair.

"You see," she went on simply, "I can come to the point. For me, everything is a lie—I am not telling this to you because I need your help, I shall never need help," she said, turning her eyes on his, "understand that from the beginning—"

"Beginning," he said in a loud voice suddenly.

"From the beginning," she repeated calmly, "right from the very start, not help but hindrance, I need enough hindrance, a total obstacle, otherwise I cannot accomplish it."

"Accomplish what, madame?" he asked and took his hand from under his beard.

"That is my affair, mine alone, that you must not question, it has nothing to do with you, you are only a means to an end."

He said, "What can I do for you?"

She smiled, a sudden smile, and under her cheek something flickered. "You can do nothing," she said and stood up. "I must always do it all—yes, I shall be your mistress—wait," she said raising her hand, and there was anger and pride in her. "Do not intrude now by word or sign, but tomorrow you will come to me—that is enough—that is all you can do," and in this word "all" he felt a limit on himself that he had never known before, and he was frightened and disquieted and unhappy.

He came the next day, cringing a little, fawning, uneasy, and she would not see him—she sent word "I do not need you yet," and he called again the next day and learned that she was out of town, then one Sunday she was in to him.

She said quietly to him, as if she were preparing him for a great disappointment, "I have deliberately, very deliberately, removed remorse from the forbidden fruit," and he was abject suddenly and trembling.

"There will be no thorns for you," she went on in a cold abrupt voice. "You will miss that, but do not presume to show it in my presence."

"Also my floor is not the floor on which you may crawl," she continued, "and I do not permit you to suffer while I am in the room—and," she added, unfastening her brooch slowly and precisely, "I dislike all spiritual odours."

"Are we all strange?" he whispered.

"It takes more than will to attain to madness."

"Yes."

Then she was silent for a while, thinking.

"I want to suffer," he murmured, and trembled again.

"We are all gross at times, but this is not your time."

"I could follow you into the wilderness."

"I would not miss you."

And it was said in a terrible forbidding voice.

"I suffer as a birthright—I want it to be something more my own than that."

"What are you going to do?" he said.

"Does one ever destroy oneself who is utterly disinterested?"

"I don't know."

Presently she said, "I love my husband—I want you to know that, it doesn't matter, but I want you to know that, and that I am content with him, and quite happy—"

"Yes," Castillion Rodkin answered and began trembling again, holding on to the sides of the bed.

"But there is something in me," she continued, "that is very mournful because it is being."

He could not answer and tears came to his eyes.

"There is another thing," she said with abrupt roughness, "that I must insist on, that is that you will not insult me by your presence while you are in this room."

He tried to stop his weeping now, and his body grew tense, abject.

"You see," she continued, "some people drink poison, some take a knife, and others drown; I take you."

In the very early dawn, she sat up with a strange smile. "Will you smoke?" she said, and lit him a cigarette. Then she withdrew into herself, sitting on the edge of the mahogany boards, her hands in her lap.

And there was a little ease, and a little comfort in Castillion Rodkin, and he turned, drawing up one foot, thrusting his hand beneath his beard, slowly smoking his cigarette.

"Does one regret?" he asked, and the figure of Katrina never moved, nor did she seem to hear.

"You know, you frightened me—last night," he went on, lying on his back now and looking at the ceiling. "I almost became something—something."

There was a long silence.

"Shall the beasts of the field and the birds of the air forsake thee?" he said gloomily, then brightly. "Shall any man forsake thee?"

Katrina Silverstaff remained as she was, but under her cheek something quivered.

The dawn was very near and the street lamps had gone out; a milk cart rattled across the square, and passed up a side street.

"One out of many, or only one?"

He put his cigarette out, he was beginning to breathe with difficulty, he was beginning to shiver.

"Well—"

He turned over, got up, stood on the floor.

"Is there nothing I can say?" he began, and went a little away and put his things on.

"When shall I see you again?"

And now a cold sweat broke out on him, and his chin trembled.

"Tomorrow?"

He tried to come toward her, but he found himself near the door instead.

"I'm nothing," he said, and turned toward her, bent slightly; he wanted to kiss her feet—but nothing helped him.

"You've taken everything now, now I cannot feel, I do not suffer—" He tried to look at her—and succeeded finally after a long time.

He could see that she did not know he was in the room.

Then something like horror entered him, and with a soft, swift running gait he reached the door, turned the handle and was gone.

A few days later, at dusk, for his heart was the heart of a dog, he came into Katrina's street, and looked at the house.

A single length of crape, bowed, hung at the door.

From that day he began to drink heavily, he got to be quite a nuisance in the cafés, he seldom had money to pay, he was a fearless beggar, almost insolent, and once when he saw Otto Silverstaff sitting alone in a corner, with his two children, he laughed a loud laugh and burst into tears.

HUSH BEFORE LOVE

———

A voice rose in the darkness saying "Love,"
And in the stall the scattered mice grew still,
Where yet the white ox slept, and on the sill
The crowing cock paused, and the grey house dove
Turned twice about upon the ledge above.

THE ROBIN'S HOUSE

———

In a stately decaying mansion, on the lower end of the Avenue, lived a woman by the name of Nelly Grissard.

Two heavy cocks stood on either side of the brownstone steps, looking out toward the park; and in the back garden a fountain, having poured out its soul for many a year, still poured, murmuring over the stomachs of the three cherubim supporting its massive basin.

Nelly Grissard was fat and lively to the point of excess. She never let a waxed floor pass under her without proving herself light of foot. Every ounce of Nelly Grissard was on the jump. Her fingers tapped, her feet fluttered, her bosom heaved; her entire diaphragm swelled with little creakings of whale-bone, lace and taffeta.

She wore feathery things about the throat, had a liking for deep burgundy silks, and wore six petticoats for the "joy of discovering that I'm not so fat as they say." She stained her good square teeth with tobacco, and cut her hair in a bang.

Nelly Grissard was fond of saying: "I'm more French than human." Her late husband had been French; had dragged his nationality about with him with the melancholy of a man who had half dropped his cloak and that cloak his life, and in the end, having wrapped it tightly about him, had departed as a Frenchman should.

There had been many "periods" in Nelly Grissard's life, a Russian, a Greek, and those privileged to look through her key-hole said, even a Chinese.

She believed in "intuition," but it was always first-hand intuition; she learned geography by a strict system of love affairs—never two men from the same part of the country.

She also liked receiving "spirit messages"—they kept her in touch with international emotion—she kept many irons in the fire and not the least of them was the "spiritual" iron.

Then she had what she called a "healing touch"—she could take away headaches, and she could tell by one pass of her hand if the bump on that particular head was a bump of genius or of avarice— or if (and she used to shudder, closing her eyes and withdrawing her hand with a slow, poised and expectant manner) it was the bump of the senses.

Nelly was, in other words, dangerously careful of her sentimentalism. No one but a sentimental woman would have called her great roomy mansion "The Robin's House," no one but a sentimentalist could possibly have lived through so many days and nights of saying "yes" breathlessly, or could have risen so often from her bed with such a magnificent and knowing air.

No one looking through the gratings of the basement window would have guessed at the fermenting mind of Nelly Grissard. Here well-starched domestics rustled about, laying cool fingers on cool fowls and frosted bottles. The cook, it is true, was a little untidy; he would come and stand in the entry, when Spring was approaching, and look over the head of Nelly Grissard's old nurse, who sat in a wheel-chair all day, her feeble hands crossed over a discarded rug of the favourite burgundy colour, staring away with half-melted eyes into the everlasting fountain, while below the cook's steaming face, on a hairy chest, rose and fell a faded holy amulet.

Sometimes the world paused to see Nelly Grissard pounce down the steps, one after another, and with a final swift and high gesture take her magnificent legs out for a drive, the coachman cracking his whip, the braided ribbons dancing at the horses' ears.

And that was about all—no, if one cared to notice, a man, in the early forties, who passed every afternoon just at four, swinging a heavy black cane.

This man was Nicholas Golwein—half Tartar, half Jew.

There was something dark, evil and obscure about Nicholas Golwein, and something bending, kindly, compassionate. Yet he was a very Jew by nature. He rode little, danced less, but smoked great self-reassuring cigars, and could out-ponder the average fidgety American by hours.

He had travelled, he had lived as the "Romans lived," and had sent many a hot-eyed girl back across the fields with something to forget or remember, according to her nature.

This man had been Nelly Grissard's lover at the most depraved period of Nelly's life. At that moment when she was colouring her drinking water green, and living on ox liver and "testina en broda," Nicholas Golwein had turned her collar back, and kissed her on that intimate portion of the throat where it has just left daylight, yet has barely passed into the shadow of the breast.

To be sure, Nelly Grissard had been depraved at an exceedingly early age, if depravity is understood to be the ability to enjoy what others shudder at, and to shudder at what others enjoy.

Nelly Grissard dreamed "absolutely honestly"—stress on the absolutely—when it was all the fashion to dream obscurely,—she could sustain the conversation just long enough not to be annoyingly brilliant, she loved to talk of ancient crimes, drawing her stomach in, and bending her fingers slightly, just slightly, but also just enough to make the guests shiver a little and think how she really should have been born in the time of the Cenci. And during the craze for Gauguin she was careful to mention that she had passed over the same South Sea roads, but where Gauguin had walked, she had been carried by two astonished donkeys.

She had been "kind" to Nicholas Golwein just long enough to make the racial melancholy blossom into a rank tall weed. He loved beautiful things, and she possessed them. He had become used to her, had "forgiven" her much (for those who had to forgive at all had to forgive Nelly in a large way), and the fact that she was too fluid to need one person's forgiveness long, drove him into slow bitterness and despair.

The fact that "her days were on her," and that she did not feel the usual woman's fear of age and dissolution, nay, that she even saw new measures to take, possessing a fertility that can only come of a decaying mind, drove him almost into insanity.

When the Autumn came, and the leaves were falling from the trees, as nature grew hot and the last flames of the season licked high among the branches, Nicholas Golwein's cheeks burned with a dull red, and he turned his eyes down.

Life did not exist for Nicholas Golwein as a matter of day and after day—it was flung at him from time to time as a cloak is flung a flunkey, and this made him proud, morose, silent.

Was it not somehow indecent that, after his forgiveness and understanding, there should be the understanding and forgiveness of another?

There was undoubtedly something cruel about Nelly Grissard's love; she took at random, and Nicholas Golwein had been the most random, perhaps, of all. The others, before him, had all been of her own class—the first had even married her, and when she finally drove him to the knife's edge, had left her a fair fortune. Nicholas Golwein had always earned his own living, he was an artist and lived as artists live. Then Nelly came—and went—and after him she had again taken one of her own kind, a wealthy Norwegian—Nord, a friend of Nicholas'.

Sometimes now Nicholas Golwein would go off into the country, trying to forget, trying to curb the tastes that Nelly's love had nourished. He nosed out small towns, but he always came hurriedly back, smelling of sassafras, the dull penetrating odour of grass, contact with trees, half-tamed animals.

The country made him think of Schubert's Unfinished Symphony—he would start running—running seemed a way to complete all that was sketchy and incomplete about nature, music, love.

"Would I recognize God if I saw him?" The joy of thinking such thoughts was not every man's, and this cheered him.

Sometimes he would go to see Nord; he was not above visiting Nelly's lover—in fact there was that between them.

He had fancied death lately. There was a tremendously sterile quality about Nicholas Golwein's fancies; they were the fancies of a race, and not of a man.

He discussed death with Nord—before the end there is something pleasant in a talk of a means to an end, and Nord had the coldness that makes death strong.

"I can hate," he would say, watching Nord out of the corner of his eye; "Nelly can't, she's too provincial—"

"Yes, there's truth in that. Nelly's good to herself—what more is there?"

"There's understanding." He meant compassion, and his eyes filled. "Does she ever speak of me?"

It was beginning to rain. Large drops struck softly against the café window and thinning out ran down upon the sill.

"Oh, yes."

"And she says?"

"Why are you never satisfied with what you have, Nicholas?"

Nicholas Golwein turned red. "One dish of cream and the cat should lick his paws into eternity. I suppose one would learn how she felt, if she feels at all, if one died."

"Why, yes, I suppose so."

They looked at each other, Nicholas Golwein in a furtive manner, moving his lips around his cigar—Nord absently, smiling a little. "Yes, that would amuse her."

"What?" Nicholas Golwein paused in his smoking and let his hot eyes rest on Nord.

"Well, if you can manage it—"

Nicholas Golwein made a gesture, shaking his cuff-links like a harness—"I can manage it," he said, wondering what Nord was thinking.

"Of course it's rather disgusting," Nord said.

"I know, I know I should go out like a gentleman, but there's more in me than the gentleman, there's something that understands meanness; a Jew can only love and be intimate with the thing that's a little abnormal, and so I love what's low and treacherous and cunning, because there's nobility and uneasiness in it for me—well," he flung out his arms—"if you were to say to Nell, 'He hung himself in the small hours, with a sheet'—what then? Everything she had ever said to me, been to me, will change for her—she won't be able to read those French journals in the same way, she won't be able to swallow water as she has always swallowed it. I know, you'll say there's nature and do you know what I'll answer: that I have a contempt for animals—just because they do not have to include Nelly Grissard's whims in their means to a living conduct—well, listen, I've made up my mind to something"—he became calm all of a sudden and looked Nord directly in the face.

"Well?"

"I shall follow you up the stairs, stand behind the door, and you shall say just these words, 'Nicholas has hung himself.'"

"And then what?"

"That's all, that's quite sufficient—then I shall know everything."

Nord stood up, letting Nicholas open the café door for him.

"You don't object?" Nicholas Golwein murmured.

Nord laughed a cold, insulting laugh. "It will amuse her—"

Nicholas nodded, "Yes, we've held the coarse essentials between our teeth like good dogs—" he said, trying to be insulting in turn, but it only sounded pathetic, sentimental.

Without a word passing between them, on the following day, they went up the stairs of Nelly Grissard's house, together. The door into the inner room was ajar, and Nicholas crept in behind this, seating himself on a little table.

He heard Nord greet Nelly, and Nelly's voice answering—"Ah, dear"—he listened no further for a moment, his mind went back, and he seemed to himself to be peaceful and happy all at once. "A binding up of old sores," he thought, a oneness with what was good and simple—with everything that evil had not contorted.

"Religion," he thought to himself, resting his chin on his hands —thinking what religion had meant to all men at all times, but to no man in his most need. "Religion is a design for pain—that's it." Then he thought, that, like all art, must be fundamentally against God—God had made his own plans—well, of that later—

Nelly had just said something—there had been a death-like silence, then her cry, but he had forgotten to listen to what it was that had passed. He changed hands on his cane. "There is someone in heaven," he found his mind saying. The rising of this feeling was pleasant—it seemed to come from the very centre of his being. "There's someone in heaven—who?" he asked himself, "who?" But there was no possible answer that was not blasphemy.

"Jews do not kill themselves—"

Nelly's voice. He smiled—there was someone in heaven, but no one here. "I'm coming," he murmured to himself—and felt a sensuous giving away in the promise.

His eyes filled. What was good in death had been used up long ago—now it was only dull repetition—death had gone beyond the need of death.

Funnily enough he thought of Nelly as she was that evening when she had something to forgive. He had pulled her toward him by one end of a burgundy ribbon, "Forgive, forgive," and she had been kind enough not to raise him, not to kiss him, saying, "I forgive"—she just stood there showing her tobacco-stained teeth in a strong laugh, "Judas eliminated." He put his hand to his mouth, "I have been *There*," and *There* seemed like a place where no one had ever been. How cruel, how monstrous!

Someone was running around the room, heavy, ponderous. "She always prided herself on her lightness of foot," and here she was running like a trapped animal, making little cries, "By the neck!"—strange words, horrifying—unreal—

"To be a little meaner than the others, a little more crafty"—well, he had accomplished that, too.

Someone must be leaning on the couch, it groaned. That took him back to Boulogne; he had loved a girl once in Boulogne, and once in the dark they had fallen, it was like falling through the sky, through the stars, finding that the stars were not only one layer thick, but that there were many layers, millions of layers, a thickness to them, and a depth—then the floor—that was like a final promise of something sordid, but lasting—firm.

Sounds rose from the streets; automobiles going uptown, horses' hoofs, a cycle siren,—that must be a child,—long drawn out, and piercing—yes, only a child would hold on to a sound like that.

"Life is life," Nelly had just said, firmly, decisively. After all he had done this well—he had never been able to think of death long, but now he had thought of it, made it pretty real—he remembered sparrows, for some unknown reason, and this worried him.

"The line of the hips, simply Renoir over again—"

They were on the familiar subject of art.

The sounds in the room twittered about him like wings in a close garden, where there is neither night nor day. "There is a power in death, even the thought of death, that is very terrible and very beautiful—" His cane slipped, and struck the floor.

"What was that?" the voice of Nelly Grissard was high, excited, startled—

"A joke."

Nicholas Golwein suddenly walked into the room.

"A joke," he said and looked at them both, smiling.

Nelly Grissard, who was on her knees, and who was holding Nord's shoe in one hand, stared at him. It seemed that she must have been about to kiss Nord's foot.

Nicholas Golwein bowed, a magnificent bow, and was about to go.

"You ought to be ashamed of yourself," Nelly Grissard cried, angrily, and got to her feet.

He began to stammer: "I—I am leaving town—I wanted to pay my respects—"

"Well, go along with you—"

Nicholas Golwein went out, shutting the door carefully behind him.

PARADISE

———

This night I've been one hour in Paradise;
There found a feather from the Cock that Crew—
There heard the echo of the Kiss that Slew,
And in the dark, about past agonies
   Hummed little flies.

NO-MAN'S-MARE

Pauvla Agrippa had died that afternoon at three; now she lay with quiet hands crossed a little below her fine breast with its transparent skin showing the veins as filmy as old lace, purple veins that were now only a system of charts indicating the pathways where her life once flowed.

Her small features were angular with that repose which she had often desired. She had not wanted to live, because she did not mind death. There were no candles about her where she lay, nor any flowers. She had said quite logically to her sisters: "Are there any candles and flowers at a birth?" They saw the point, but regretted the philosophy, for buying flowers would have connected them with Pauvla Agrippa, in this, her new adventure.

Pauvla Agrippa's hair lay against her cheeks like pats of plated butter; the long golden ends tucked in and wound about her head and curved behind her neck. Pauvla Agrippa had once been complimented on her fine black eyes and this yellow hair of hers, and she had smiled and been quite pleased, but had drawn attention to the fact that she had also another quite remarkable set of differences—her small thin arms with their tiny hands and her rather long narrow feet.

She said that she was built to remain standing; now she could rest.

Her sister, Tasha, had been going about all day, praying to different objects in search of one that would give her comfort, though she was not so much grieved as she might have been, because Pauvla Agrippa had been so curious about all this.

True, Agrippa's husband seemed lost, and wandered about like a restless dog, trying to find a spot that would give him relief as he smoked.

One of Pauvla's brothers was playing on the floor with Pauvla's baby. This baby was small and fat and full of curves. His arms curved above his head, and his legs curved downward, including his picture book and rattle in their oval. He shouted from time to time at his uncle, biting the buttons on his uncle's jacket. This baby and this boy had one thing in common—a deep curiosity—a sense that somewhere that curiosity would be satisfied. They had all accomplished something. Pauvla Agrippa and her husband and her sister and the boy and Pauvla's baby, but still there was incompleteness about everything.

Nothing was ever done; there wasn't such a thing as rest, that was certain, for the sister still felt that her prayers were not definite, the husband knew he would smoke again after lunch, the boy knew he was only beginning something, as the baby also felt it, and Pauvla Agrippa herself, the seemingly most complete, had yet to be buried. Her body was confronted with the eternal necessity of change.

It was all very sad and puzzling, and rather nice too. After all, atoms were the only things that had imperishable existence, and therefore were the omnipotent quality and quantity—God should be recognized as something that was everywhere in millions, irrevocable and ineradicable—one single great thing has always been the prey of the million little things. The beasts of the jungle are laid low by the insects. Yes, she agreed that everything was multiple that counted. Pauvla was multiple now, and some day they would be also. This was the reason that she wandered from room to room touching things, vases, candlesticks, tumblers, knives, forks, the holy pictures and statues and praying to each of them, praying for a great thing, to many presences.

A neighbour from across the way came to see them while Pauvla's brother was still playing with the baby. This man was a farmer, once upon a time, and liked to remember it, as city-bred men in the country like to remember New York and its sophistication.

He spent his Summers, however, in the little fishing village where the sisters, Pauvla and Tasha, had come to know him. He always spoke of "going toward the sea." He said that there was something more than wild about the ocean; it struck him as being a little unnatural, too.

He came in now grumbling and wiping his face with a coarse red handkerchief, remarking on the "catch" and upon the sorrow of the house of Agrippa, all in the one breath.

"There's a touch of damp in the air," he said, sniffing, his nose held back so that his small eyes gleamed directly behind it. "The fish have been bad catching and no-man's-mare is going up the headlands, her tail stretched straight out."

Tasha came forward with cakes and tea and paused, praying over them also, still looking for comfort. She was a small woman, with a round, wrinkled forehead and the dark eyes of her sister; today she felt inconvenienced because she could not understand her own feelings—once or twice she had looked upon the corpse with resentment because it had done something to Pauvla; however, she was glad to see the old man, and she prayed to him silently also, to see if it would help. Just what she prayed for she could not tell; the words she used were simple: "What is it, what is it?" over and over with her own childhood prayers to end with.

She had a great deal of the quietness of this village about her, the quietness that is in the roaring of the sea and the wind, and when she sighed it was like the sound made of great waters running back to sea between the narrow sides of little stones.

It was here that she, as well as her brothers and sisters, had been born. They fished in the fishing season and sold to the market at one-eighth of the market price, but when the markets went so low that selling would put the profits down for months, they turned the nets over and sent the fish back to sea.

Today Tasha was dressed in her ball-gown; she had been anticipating a local gathering that evening and then Pauvla Agrippa got her heart attack and died. This dress was low about the shoulders, with flounces of taffeta, and the sea-beaten face of Tasha rose out of its stiff elegance like a rock from heavy moss. Now that she had brought the cakes and tea, she sat listening to this neighbour as he spoke French to her younger brother.

When they spoke in this strange language she was always surprised to note that their voices became unfamiliar to her—she could not have told which was which, or if they were themselves at all. Closing her eyes, she tried to see if this would make any difference, and it didn't. Then she slowly raised her small plump hands and pressed them to her ears—this was better, because now she could not tell that it was French that they were speaking, it was sound only and might have been anything, and again she sighed, and was glad that they were less strange to her; she could not bear this strangeness today, and wished they would stop speaking in a foreign tongue.

"What are you saying?" she enquired, taking the teacup in one hand, keeping the other over her ear.

"Talking about the horse," he said, and went on.

Again Tasha became thoughtful. This horse that they were speaking about had been on the sands, it seemed to her, for as long as she could remember. It was a wild thing belonging to nobody. Sometimes in a coming storm, she had seen it standing with its head out toward the waters, its mane flying in the light air, and its thin sides fluttering with the beating of its heart.

It was old now, with sunken flanks and knuckled legs; it no longer stood straight—and the hair about its nose had begun to turn grey. It never interfered with the beach activities, and on the other hand it never permitted itself to be touched. Early in her memory of this animal, Tasha had tried to stroke it, but it had started, arched its neck and backed away from her with hurried jumping steps. Many of the ignorant fisherfolk had called it the sea horse and also "no-man's-mare." They began to fear it, and several of them thought it a bad omen.

Tasha knew better—sometimes it would be down upon the pebbly part of the shore, its head laid flat as though it were dead, but no one could approach within fifty feet without its instantly leaping up and standing with its neck thrust forward and its brown eyes watching from beneath the coarse lashes.

In the beginning people had tried to catch it and make it of use. Gradually everyone in the village had made the attempt; not one of them had ever succeeded.

The large black nostrils were always wet, and they shook as though someone were blowing through them—great nostrils like black flowers.

This mare was old now and did not get up so often when approached. Tasha had been as near to it as ten paces, and Pauvla Agrippa had once approached so near that she could see that its eyes were failing, that a thin mist lay over its right eyeball, so that it seemed to be flirting with her, and this made her sad and she hurried away, and she thought, "The horse had its own defence; when it dies it will be so horrifying perhaps that not one of us will approach it." Though many had squabbled about which of them should have its long beautiful tail.

Pauvla Agrippa's husband had finished his cigar and came in now, bending his head to get through the low casement. He spoke to the neighbour a few moments and then sat down beside his sister-in-law.

He began to tell her that something would have to be done with Pauvla, and added that they would have to manage to get her over to the undertaker's at the end of the headland, but that they had no means of conveyance. Tasha thought of this horse because she had been thinking about it before he interrupted and she spoke of it timidly, but it was only an excuse to say something.

"You can't catch it," he said, shaking his head.

Here the neighbour broke in: "It's easy enough to catch it; this last week three children have stroked it—it's pretty low, I guess; but I doubt if it would be able to walk that far."

He looked over the rim of the teacup to see how this remark would be taken—he felt excited all of a sudden at the thought that something was going to be attempted that had not been attempted in many years, and a feeling of misfortune took hold of him that he had certainly not felt at Pauvla Agrippa's death. Everything about the place, and his life that had seemed to him quite normal and natural, now seemed strange.

The disrupting of one idea—that the horse could not be caught —put him into a mood that made all other accustomed things alien.

However, after this it seemed quite natural that they should make the effort and Tasha went into the room where Pauvla Agrippa lay.

The boy had fallen asleep in the corner and Pauvla's baby was crawling over him, making for Pauvla, cooing softly and saying "mamma" with difficulty, because the little under-lip kept reaching to the upper lip to prevent the saliva from interrupting the call.

Tasha put her foot in the baby's way and stood looking down at Pauvla Agrippa, where her small hands lay beneath her fine breast with its purple veins, and now Tasha did not feel quite the same resentment that she had felt earlier. It is true this body had done something irrevocable to Pauvla Agrippa, but she also realized that she, Tasha, must now do something to this body; it was the same with everything, nothing was left as it was, something was always altering something else. Perhaps it was an unrecognized law.

Pauvla Agrippa's husband had gone out to see what could be done with the mare, and now the neighbour came in, saying that it would not come in over the sand, but that he—the husband— thought that it would walk toward the headland, as it was wont.

"If you could only carry her out to it," he said.

Tasha called in two of her brothers and woke up the one on the floor. "Everything will be arranged for her comfort," she said, "when we get her up there." They lifted Pauvla Agrippa up and her baby began to laugh, asking to be lifted up also, and holding its little hands high that it might be lifted, but no one was paying any attention to him, because now they were moving his mother.

Pauvla Agrippa looked fine as they carried her, only her small hands parted and deserted the clef where they had lain, dropping down upon the shoulders of her brothers. Several children stood hand in hand watching, and one or two villagers appeared who had heard from the neighbours what was going on.

The mare had been induced to stand and someone had slipped a halter over its neck for the first time in many years; there was a frightened look in the one eye and the film that covered the other seemed to darken, but it made no objection when they raised Pauvla Agrippa and placed her on its back, tying her on with a fish net.

Then someone laughed, and the neighbour slapped his leg saying, "Look what the old horse has come to—caught and burdened at last." And he watched the mare with small cruel eyes.

Pauvla Agrippa's husband took the strap of the halter and began plodding through the sand, the two boys on either side of the horse holding to all that was left of Pauvla Agrippa. Tasha came behind, her hands folded, praying now to this horse, still trying to find peace, but she noticed with a little apprehension that the horse's flanks had begun to quiver, and that this quiver was extending to its ribs and from its ribs to its forelegs.

Then she saw it turn a little, lifting its head. She called out to Pauvla Agrippa's husband who, startled with the movement and the cry, dropped the rope.

The mare had turned toward the sea; for an instant it stood there, quivering, a great thin, bony thing with crooked legs; its blind eyes half covered with the black coarse lashes. Pauvla Agrippa with her head thrown a bit back rested easily, it seemed, the plaits of her yellow hair lying about her neck, but away from her face, because she was not supported quite right; still she looked like some strange new sea animal beneath the net that held her from falling.

Then without warning, no-man's-mare jumped forward and plunged neck-deep into the water.

A great wave came up, covered it, receded and it could be seen swimming, its head out of the water, while Pauvla Agrippa's loosened yellow hair floated behind. No one moved. Another wave rose high, descended, and again the horse was seen swimming with head up, and this time Pauvla Agrippa's hands were parted and lay along the water as though she were swimming.

The most superstitious among them began crossing themselves, and one woman dropped on her knees, rocking from side to side; and still no one moved.

And this time the wave rose, broke and passed on, leaving the surface smooth.

That night Tasha picked up Pauvla Agrippa's sleepy boy and standing in the doorway prayed to the sea, and this time she found comfort.

SIX SONGS OF KHALIDINE

———

To the Memory of Mary Pyne

The flame of your red hair does crawl and creep
Upon your body that denies the gloom
And feeds upon your flesh as 't would consume
The cold precision of your austere sleep—
And all night long I beat it back, and weep.

It is not gentleness but mad despair
That sets us kissing mouths, O Khalidine,
Your mouth and mine, and one sweet mouth unseen
We call our soul. Yet thick within our hair
The dusty ashes that our days prepare.

The dark comes up, my little love, and dyes
Your fallen lids with stain of ebony,
And draws a thread of fear 'tween you and me
Pulling thin blindness down across our eyes—
And far within the vale a lost bird cries.

Does not the wind moan round your painted towers
Like rats within an empty granary?
The clapper lost, and long blown out to sea
Your windy doves. And here the black bat cowers
Against your clock that never strikes the hours.

And now I say, has not the mountain's base
Here trembled long ago unto the cry
"I love you, ah, I love you!" Now we die
And lay, all silent, to the earth our face.
Shall that cast out the echo of this place?

Has not one in the dark funereal
Heard foot-fall fearful, born of no man's tread,
And felt the wings of death, though no wing spread
And on his cheek a tear, though no tear fell—
And a voice saying without breath "Farewell!"

THE DOVE

———

PERSONS:

AMELIA BURGSON
VERA BURGSON | *Sisters*

THE DOVE | *A young girl living with the* BURGSONS

TIME—*Early morning*

PLACE—*The* BURGSON *Apartment, a long, low rambling affair at the top of a house in the heart of the city.*

The decoration is garish, dealing heavily in reds and pinks. There is an evident attempt to make the place look luxuriously sensual. The furniture is all of the reclining type.

The walls are covered with a striped paper in red and white. Only two pictures are evident, one of the Madonna and child, and one of an early English tandem race.

There are firearms everywhere. Many groups of swords, ancient and modern, are secured to the walls. A pistol or two lie in chairs, etc.

There is only one door, which leads out into the back hall directly back centre.

AMELIA BURGSON *is a woman rather over the normal in height, with large braids of very yellow hair, done about a long face. She seems vitally hysterical.*

VERA BURGSON *is small, thin and dark.*

THE DOVE *is a slight girl barely out of her teens; she is as delicate as china with almost dangerously transparent skin. Her nose is high-bridged and thin, her hands and feet are also very long and delicate. She has red hair, very elegantly coiffured. When she moves seldom. The slightest line runs between her legs, giving her the expectant waiting air of a deer.*

At the rising of the curtain THE DOVE, *gowned in white, is seated on the divan polishing the blade of an immense sword. Half reclining to her right lies* VERA *in a thin yellow morning gown. A French novel has half fallen from her hand. Her eyes are closed.*

THE DOVE—Yes, I'm hurrying.

VERA—That's best, she will be back soon.

THE DOVE—She is never gone long.

VERA—No, never very long—one would grow old waiting for the day on which she would stay an hour—a whole hour.

THE DOVE—Yes, that's true.

VERA—[*Wearily.*] She says we live dangerously; [*laughs*] why, we can't even keep the flies out.

THE DOVE—Yes, there are a great many flies.

VERA—[*After a pause.*] Shall I ever have a lover, do you suppose?

141

THE DOVE—[*Turning the sword over.*] No, I suppose not.

VERA—Yet Amelia and I have made it our business to know —everything.

THE DOVE—Yes?

VERA—Yes. We say this little thing in French and that little thing in Spanish, and we collect knives and pistols, but we only shoot our buttons off with the guns and cut our darning cotton with the knives, and we'll never, never be perverse though our entire education has been about knees and garters and pinches on hind-quarters—elegantly bestowed—and we keep a few animals—very badly—hoping to see something first-hand—and our beds are as full of yellow pages and French jokes as a bird's nest is full of feathers—God! [*She stands up abruptly*] Little one, why do I wear lace at my elbows?

THE DOVE—You have pretty arms.

VERA—Nonsense! Lace swinging back and forth like that, tickling my arms, well, that's not beauty—

THE DOVE—I know.

VERA—[*Returning to her couch.*] I sometimes wonder what you do know, you are such a strange happening, anyway. Well then, tell me what you think of me and what you think of my sister, you have been here long enough. Why do you stay? Do you love us?

THE DOVE—I love something that you have.

VERA—What?

THE DOVE—Your religious natures.

VERA—Good heavens!

THE DOVE—You misunderstand me. I call that imagination that is the growth of ignorance, religion.

VERA—And why do you like that?

THE DOVE—Because it goes farther than knowledge.

VERA—You know, sometimes I wish—

THE DOVE—Yes?

VERA—That you had lived all we pretend we have.

THE DOVE—Why?

VERA—I don't know, but somehow someone like you should know —everything.

THE DOVE—Do I seem so young?

VERA—I know, that's what's so odd. [*Impatiently.*] For heaven's sake, will you stop polishing that infernal weapon!

THE DOVE—[*Quietly.*] She said to me: "Take all the blood stains off first, then polish it."

VERA—There you are; she is quite mad, there's no doubt. Blood stains! Why, she would be afraid to cut her chops with it—and as for the rest of her manifestations—nonsense!

THE DOVE—She carries a pistol with her, just to go around the corner for a pound of butter.

VERA—It's wicked! She keeps an enormous blunderbuss in the corner of her room, but when I make up her bed, all I find is some Parisienne bathing girl's picture stuck full of pin holes—

THE DOVE—I know, she sits beside me for hours making those pin holes in the borders of everything in sight.

VERA—[*With a strange anger.*] Why do you stay?

THE DOVE—Why should I go?

VERA—I should think this house and two such advanced virgins as Amelia and myself would drive you to despair—

THE DOVE—No, no, I'm not driven to despair—

VERA—What do you find here?

THE DOVE—I love Amelia.

VERA—Another reason for going away.

THE DOVE—Is it?

VERA—Yes, it is.

THE DOVE—Strange, I don't feel that way about it.

VERA—Sometimes I think—

THE DOVE—Yes?

VERA—That you are the mad one, and that we are just eccentric.

THE DOVE—Yet my story is quite simple.

VERA—I'm not so certain.

THE DOVE—Yet you have heard it.

VERA—There's more than one hears.

THE DOVE—I was born on a farm—

VERA—So you say.

THE DOVE—I became very fond of moles—it's so daring of them to be in the darkness underground. And then I like the open fields, too—they say there's nothing like nature for the simple spirit.

VERA—Yes, and I've long had my suspicions of nature.

THE DOVE—Be that as it may, my brothers were fond of me—in a way, and my father in—a way—then I came to New York—

VERA—And took up the painting of china—

THE DOVE—Exactly. I was at that for three years, then one day I met you walking through the park, do you remember? You had a parasol, you tipped it back of your head, you looked at me a long time. Then I met Amelia, by the same high fence in the same park, and I bowed to her in an almost military fashion, my heels close together—

VERA—And you never did anything wild, insane—

THE DOVE—It depends on what you call wild, insane—

VERA—[*With great excitement.*] Have you ever taken opium or hasheesh?

THE DOVE—[*As if answering.*] There are many kinds of dreams—in one you laugh, in another you weep—

VERA—[*Wringing her hands.*] Yes, yes, once I dreamed. A dream in the day, with my eyes wide open. I dreamt I was a Dresden doll and that I had been blown down by the wind and that I broke all to pieces—that is, my arms and my head broke all to pieces—but that I was surprised to find that my china skirt had become flexible, as if it were made of chiffon and lace.

THE DOVE—You see, there are many dreams—

VERA—Have you ever felt that your bones were utterly sophisticated but that your flesh was keeping them from expressing themselves?

THE DOVE—Or vice versa?

VERA—Yes, or vice versa.

THE DOVE—There are many kinds of dreams—

VERA—You know, I'm afraid of you!

THE DOVE—Me?

VERA—Yes, you seem so gentle—do we not call you the Dove? And you are so little—so little it's almost immoral, you make me feel as if—

THE DOVE—As if?

VERA—Well, as if your terrible quality were not one of action, but just the opposite, as if you wanted to prevent nothing.

THE DOVE—There are enough people preventing things, aren't there?

VERA—Yes—that's why you frighten me.

THE DOVE—Because I let everything go on, as far as it can go?

VERA—Yes, because you disturb nothing.

THE DOVE—I see.

VERA—You never meddle—

THE DOVE—No, I never meddle.

VERA—You don't even observe as other people do, you don't watch. Why, if I were to come to you, wringing my hands saying, "Amelia has shot herself," I don't believe you would stand up.

THE DOVE—No, I don't suppose I would, but I would do something for all that.

VERA—What?

THE DOVE—I should want to be very sure you wrung your hands as much as possible, and that Amelia had gotten all there was to get out of the bullet before she died.

VERA—It's all very well, but why don't you do something?

THE DOVE—A person who is capable of anything needs no practice.

VERA—You are probably maligning yourself, you are a gentle creature, a very girl—

THE DOVE—If you were sensitive you would not say that.

VERA—Well, perhaps. [*She laughs a hard laugh.*] What can you expect of a lumber dealer's daughter?

THE DOVE—Why are you so restless, Vera?

VERA—Because I'm a woman. I leave my life entirely to my imagination and my imagination is terrific. I can't even turn to religion for the *prie-dieu* inclines me to one thing only—so there you are!

THE DOVE—You imagine—many things?

VERA—You know well enough—sitting here day after day, giving my mind everything to do, the body nothing—

THE DOVE—What do you want, Vera?

VERA—Some people would say a lover, but I don't say a lover; some people would say a home, but I don't say a home. You see I have imagined myself beyond the need of the usual home and beyond the reach of the usual lover—

THE DOVE—Then?

VERA—Perhaps what I really want is a reason for using one of these pistols! [*She laughs and lies back.* THE DOVE, *having risen, goes up behind* VERA *and places her hand on her throat.*]

THE DOVE—Now you may use one of those pistols.

VERA—[*Startled, but making no attempt to remove the* DOVE'S *hand.*] For such a *little* thing?

THE DOVE—[*Dropping her hand, once more taking up her old position, sword on knee.*] Ah!

VERA—Why do you say that? [*She is evidently agitated.*]

THE DOVE—I suppose I shall *always* wait.

VERA—What is the matter?

THE DOVE—Always, always!

VERA—What *is* the matter?

THE DOVE—I suppose I'm waiting for the person who will know that anything is a reason for using a pistol, unless one is waiting for the obvious, and the obvious has never been sufficient reason.

VERA—It's all hopeless, I am hopeless and Amelia is hopeless, and as for you—[*She makes a gesture.*]

THE DOVE—I've never held anything against hopelessness.

VERA—Now what do you mean?

THE DOVE—It doesn't matter.

VERA—[*After a long pause.*] I wish you danced.

THE DOVE—Perhaps I do.

VERA—It might make me happier.

THE DOVE—[*Irrelevantly.*] Why don't people get angry at each other, quite suddenly and without reason?

VERA—Why should they?

THE DOVE—Isn't there something fine and cold and detached about a causeless anger?

VERA—I suppose so, it depends—

THE DOVE—No, it does not depend, that's exactly it; to have a reason is to cheapen rage. I wish every man were beyond the reach of his own biography.

VERA—You are either quite an idiot, or a saint.

THE DOVE—I thought we had discussed that.

VERA—[*Dashed but not showing it.*] Yes, a saint.

THE DOVE—[*Continuing.*] I'm impatient of necessary continuity, I'm too sensitive, perhaps. I want the beautiful thing to be, how can logic have anything to do with it, or probable sequence?

VERA—You make my hair stand on end!

THE DOVE—Of course, that's logical!

VERA—Then how is it you like Amelia? And how do you stand me?

THE DOVE—Because you are two splendid dams erected about two little puddles.

VERA—You're horrid!

THE DOVE—Only horrid!

VERA—Yes, I'm really afraid of you.

THE DOVE—Afraid?

VERA—For instance, when you're out of this room all these weapons might be a lot of butter knives or pop guns, but let you come in—

THE DOVE—Well?

VERA—It becomes an arsenal.

THE DOVE—Yet you call me the Dove.

VERA—Amelia called you the Dove, I'd never have thought of it. It's just like Amelia to call the only dangerous thing she ever knew the "Dove."

THE DOVE—Yes, there's something in that.

VERA—Shall I sing for you?

THE DOVE—If you like.

VERA—Or shall I show you the album that no one ever sees? [*She laughs.*] If we had any friends we would have to throw that book in the fire.

THE DOVE—And you would have to clear the entry—

VERA—True. It's because of that picture of the Venetian courtesans that I send Amelia out for the butter, I don't dare let the grocer call.

THE DOVE—You have cut yourselves off—just because you're lonely.

VERA—Yes, just because we are lonely.

THE DOVE—It's quite wonderful.

VERA—It's a wonder the neighbours don't complain of Amelia's playing that way on the violin.

THE DOVE—I had not noticed.

VERA—No, I presume not, but everyone else in the house has. No nice woman slurs as many notes as Amelia does! [*At this moment* AMELIA *enters the outer room. She is wearing a cloak with three shoulder-capes, a large plumed hat, and skirt with many flounces.*]

AMELIA—[*From the entry.*] You should come and see Carpaccio's Deux Courtisanes Vénitiennes now, the sun is shining right in on the head of the one in the foreground. [*She begins to hum an Italian street song.*] Well, I have brought a little something and a bottle of wine. The wine is for you, my Dove—and for you, Vera, I've a long green feather. [*Pause in which* THE DOVE *continues to polish the blade of the sword.* VERA *has picked up her book.*]

AMELIA—[*Advancing into the room, shrugging.*] It's damp! [*Seeing* THE DOVE *still at work.*] What a sweet, gentle creature, what a little Dove it is! Ah, God, it's a sin, truly it's a sin that I, a woman with temperament, permit a young girl to stay in the same room with me!

THE DOVE—[*In a peaceful voice.*] I've loaded all the pistols—

VERA—[*With suppressed anger.*] Shined all the swords, ground all the poniard points! Attack a man now if you dare, he'll think you're playing with him!

AMELIA—[*In an awful voice.*] Vera! [*She begins pacing.*] Disaster! disaster!—wherever I go, disaster! A woman selling fish tried to do me out of a quarter and when I remonstrated with her, she said with a wink: "I, too, have been bitten by the fox!"

THE DOVE—If you'll sit down I'll make some tea.

AMELIA—No, no, we'll have a little lunch soon, only I never can get the corks out of bottles.

THE DOVE—I can.

VERA—Rubbish! [*She gets up and goes out.*]

AMELIA—Well, has anything happened since I went out?

THE DOVE—No.

AMELIA—No, no, it never does. [*She begins to walk about hurriedly.*] Aren't there a great many flies in here?

THE DOVE—Yes, the screens should be put up.

AMELIA—No, no, no, I don't want anything to be shut out. Flies have a right to more than life, they have a right to be curious.

THE DOVE—A bat flew into the room last night.

AMELIA—[*Shuddering.*] Some day I shall look like a bat, having beaten my wings about every corner of the world, and never having hung over anything but myself—

THE DOVE—And this morning, early, before you got up, the little seamstress' monkey walked in through the window—

AMELIA—[*Stopping short.*] Are we to become infested?

THE DOVE—Yesterday the mail-man offered me some dancing mice, he's raising them.

AMELIA—[*Throwing up her hands.*] There! You see! [*Pause.*] Why should I wear red heels? Why does my heart beat?

THE DOVE—Red heels are handsome.

AMELIA—Yes, yes, that's what I say [*she begins to dance*]. Little one, were you ever held in the arms of the one you love?

THE DOVE—Who knows?

AMELIA—If we had not been left an income we might have been in danger—well, let us laugh. [*She takes a few more dance steps*]. Eating makes one fat, nothing more, and exercising reduces one, nothing more. Drink wine—put flesh on the instep, the instep that used to tell such a sweet story—and then the knees—fit for nothing but prayers! The hands—too fat to wander! [*She waves her arm*]. Then one exercises, but it's never the same; what one has, is always better than what one regains. Is it not so, my little one? But never mind, don't answer. I'm in an excellent humour—I could talk for hours, all about myself—to myself, for myself. God! I'd like to tear out all the wires in the house! Destroy all the tunnels in the city, leave nothing underground or hidden or useful, oh, God, God! [*She has danced until she comes directly in front of* THE DOVE. *She drops on her knees and lays her arms on either side of* THE DOVE.] I hate the chimneys on the houses, I hate the doorways, I hate you, I hate Vera, but most of all I hate my red heels!

THE DOVE—[*Almost inaudibly.*] Now, now!

AMELIA—[*In high excitement.*] Give me the sword! It has been sharpened long enough, give it to me, give it to me! [*She makes a blind effort to find the sword; finding* THE DOVE'S *hand instead, she clutches it convulsively. Slowly* THE DOVE *bares Amelia's left shoulder and breast, and leaning down, sets her teeth in. Amelia gives a slight, short stifled cry. At the same moment* VERA *appears in the doorway with the uncorked bottle.* THE DOVE *stands up swiftly, holding a pistol. She turns in the doorway hastily vacated by* VERA.]

THE DOVE—So! [*She bows, a deep military bow, and turning goes into the entry.*]

THE VOICE OF THE DOVE—For the house of Burgson! [*A moment later a shot is heard.*]

AMELIA—[*Running after her.*] Oh, my God!

VERA—What has she done?

AMELIA—[*Reappearing in the doorway with the picture of the Venetian courtesans, through which there is a bullet hole—slowly, but with emphasis.*] This *is obscene!*

CURTAIN

MOTHER

————

A feeble light flickered in the pawn shop at Twenty-nine. Usually, in the back of this shop, reading by this light—a rickety lamp with a common green cover—sat Lydia Passova, the mistress.

Her long heavy head was divided by straight bound hair. Her high firm bust was made still higher and still firmer by German corsets. She was excessively tall, due to extraordinarily long legs. Her eyes were small, and not well focused. The left was slightly distended from the long use of a magnifying glass.

She was middle-aged, and very slow in movement, though well balanced. She wore coral in her ears, a coral necklace, and many coral finger rings.

There was about her jewelry some of the tragedy of all articles that find themselves in pawn, and she moved among the trays like the guardians of cemetery grounds, who carry about with them some of the lugubrious stillness of the earth on which they have been standing.

She dealt, in most part, in cameos, garnets, and a great many inlaid bracelets and cuff-links. There were a few watches however, and silver vessels and fishing tackle and faded slippers—and when, at night, she lit the lamp, these and the trays of precious and semi-precious stones, and the little ivory crucifixes, one on either side of the window, seemed to be leading a swift furtive life of their own, conscious of the slow pacing woman who was known to the street as Lydia Passova.

No one knew her, not even her lover—a little nervous fellow, an Englishman quick in speech with a marked accent, a round-faced

youth with a deep soft cleft in his chin, on which grew two separate tufts of yellow hair. His eyes were wide and pale, and his
eyeteeth prominent.

He dressed in tweeds, walked with the toes in, seemed sorrow-
ful when not talking, laughed a great deal and was nearly always to
be found in the café about four of an afternoon.

When he spoke it was quick and jerky. He had spent a great
deal of his time in Europe, especially the watering places—and had
managed to get himself in trouble in St. Moritz, it was said, with a
well-connected family.

He liked to seem a little eccentric and managed it simply
enough while in America. He wore no hat, and liked to be found
reading the *London Times*, under a park lamp at three in the
morning.

Lydia Passova was never seen with him. She seldom left her
shop; however, she was always pleased when he wanted to go anywhere: "Go," she would say, kissing his hand, "and when you are
tired come back."

Sometimes she would make him cry. Turning around she
would look at him a little surprised, with lowered lids, and a light
tightening of the mouth.

"Yes," he would say, "I know I'm trivial—well then, here I go,
I will leave you, not disturb you any longer!" and darting for the
door he would somehow end by weeping with his head buried in
her lap.

She would say, "There, there—why are you so nervous?"

And he would laugh again: "My father was a nervous man, and
my mother was high-strung, and as for me—" He would not finish.

Sometimes he would talk to her for long hours, she seldom
answering, occupied with her magnifying glass and her rings, but
in the end she was sure to send him out with: "That's all very true,
I have no doubt; now go out by yourself and think it over"—and
he would go, with something like relief, embracing her large hips
with his small strong arms.

They had known each other a very short time, three or four
months. He had gone in to pawn his little gold ring, he was always

in financial straits, though his mother sent him five pounds a week; and examining the ring, Lydia Passova had been so quiet, inevitable, necessary, that it seemed as if he must have known her forever—"at some time," as he said.

Yet they had never grown together. They remained detached, and on her part, quiet, preoccupied.

He never knew how much she liked him. She never told him; if he asked she would look at him in that surprised manner, drawing her mouth together.

In the beginning he had asked her a great many times, clinging to her, and she moved about arranging her trays with a slight smile, and in the end lowered her hand and stroked him gently.

He immediately became excited. "Let us dance," he cried, "I have a great capacity for happiness."

"Yes, you are very happy," she said.

"You understand, don't you?" he asked abruptly.

"What?"

"That my tears are nothing, have no significance, they are just a protective fluid—when I see anything happening that is about to affect my happiness I cry, that's all."

"Yes," Lydia Passova said, "I understand." She turned around reaching up to some shelves, and over her shoulder she asked, "Does it hurt?"

"No, it only frightens me. You never cry, do you?"

"No, I never cry."

That was all. He never knew where she had come from, what her life had been, if she had or had not been married, if she had or had not known lovers; all that she would say was, "Well, you are with me, does that tell you nothing?" and he had to answer, "No, it tells me nothing."

When he was sitting in the café he often thought to himself, "There's a great woman"—and he was a little puzzled why he thought this because his need of her was so entirely different from any need he seemed to remember having possessed before.

There was no swagger in him about her, the swagger he had always felt for his conquests with women. Yet there was not a trace of shame—he was neither proud nor shy about Lydia Passova, he was something entirely different. He could not have said himself what his feeling was—but it was in no way disturbing.

People had, it is true, begun to tease him:

"You're a devil with the ladies."

Where this had made him proud, now it made him uneasy.

"Now, there's a certain Lydia Passova for instance, who would ever have thought—"

Furious he would rise.

"So, you do feel—"

He would walk away, stumbling a little among the chairs, putting his hand on the back of every one on the way to the door.

Yet he could see that, in her time, Lydia Passova had been a "perverse" woman—there was, about everything she did, an economy that must once have been a very sensitive and a very sensuous impatience, and because of this everyone who saw her felt a personal loss.

Sometimes, tormented, he would come running to her, stopping abruptly, putting it to her this way:

"Somebody has said something to me."

"When—where?"

"Now, in the café."

"What?"

"I don't know, a reproach—"

She would say:

"We are all, unfortunately, only what we are."

She had a large and beautiful angora cat, it used to sit in the tray of amethysts and opals and stare at her from very bright cold eyes. One day it died, and calling her lover to her she said:

"Take her out and bury her." And when he had buried her he came back, his lips twitching.

"You loved that cat—this will be a great loss."

"Have I a memory?" she inquired.

"Yes," he answered.

"Well," she said quietly, fixing her magnifying glass firmly in her eye. "We have looked at each other, that is enough."

And then one day she died.

The caretaker of the furnace came to him, where he was sipping his liqueur as he talked to his cousin, a pretty little blond girl, who had a boring and comfortably provincial life, and who was beginning to chafe.

He got up, trembling, pale, and hurried out.

The police were there, and said they thought it had been heart failure.

She lay on the couch in the inner room. She was fully dressed, even to her coral ornaments; her shoes were neatly tied—large bows of a ribbed silk.

He looked down. Her small eyes were slightly open, the left, that had used the magnifying glass, was slightly wider than the other. For a minute she seemed quite natural. She had the look of one who is about to say: "Sit beside me."

Then he felt the change. It was in the peculiar heaviness of the head—sensed through despair and not touch. The high breasts looked very still, the hands were half closed, a little helpless, as in life—hands that were too proud to "hold." The drawn-up limb exposed a black petticoat and a yellow stocking. It seemed that she had become hard—set, as in a mould—that she rejected everything now, but in rejecting had bruised him with a last terrible pressure. He moved and knelt down. He shivered. He put his closed hands to his eyes. He could not weep.

She was an old woman, he could see that. The ceasing of that one thing that she could still have for anyone made it simple and direct.

Something oppressed him, weighed him down, bent his shoulders, closed his throat. He felt as one feels who has become conscious of passion for the first time, in the presence of a relative.

He flung himself on his face, like a child.

That night, however, he wept, lying in bed, his knees drawn up.

SONG IN AUTUMN

———

The wind comes down before the creeping night
And you, my love, are hid within the green
Long grasses; and the dusk steals up between
Each leaf, as through the shadow quick with fright
The startled hare leaps up and out of sight.

The hedges whisper in their loaded boughs
Where warm birds slumber, pressing wing to wing,
All pulsing faintly, like a muted string
Above us where we weary of our vows—
And hidden underground the soft moles drowse.

THE NIGGER

———

John Hardaway was dying. That wasn't what he minded. His small, well-shaped hands twitched at the soft coverlet which rose and fell slowly with his breathing, and he breathed hard with mouth open, showing all his teeth.

Rabb, the nigger, crouched in the corner. The air about her was heavy with her odour. She kept blinking her eyes. She was awed at the presence of her master, but ashamed too, ashamed that he was dying—ashamed as she would have been had he been caught at his toilet.

Rabb was a good nigger; she had served John Hardaway's mother, she had seen her die—old Mrs. Hardaway fluttered against her lace like a bird caught in deep foliage—Rabb had been able to do something about Mrs. Hardaway's death because Mrs. Hardaway had loved her, in her way.

Mrs. Hardaway had died understandably—she had breathed hard too, opening her mouth, but it was gentle and eager, like a child at the breast.

Rabb had tried to be near her, had put her hands on her. But the thing she was trying to touch lay in some hidden corner of Mrs. Hardaway, as a cat hides away under a bed, and Rabb had done nothing after all.

But it was different with John Hardaway. She watched life playing coquettishly with him. It played with him as a dog plays with an old coat. It shook him suddenly in great gusts of merriment. It played with his eyelids; it twisted his mouth, it went in and out of his body, like a flame running through a funnel—throwing him utterly aside in the end, leaving him cold, lonely, and forbidding.

John Hardaway hated negroes with that hate a master calls love. He was a Southerner and never forgot it. Rabb had nursed him when he was an infant, she had seen him grow up into a big boy, and then she had been there when he broke his mistress's back by some flaw in his otherwise flawless passion.

From time to time John Hardaway called for water. And when Rabb tried to lift his head, he cursed her for a 'black bitch'—but in the end he had to let her hold it.

John Hardaway was fifty-nine, he had lived well, scornfully, and this always makes the end easier; he had been a gentleman in the only way a Southerner has of being one—he never forgot that he was a Hardaway—

He called out to her now:

"When I die—leave the room."

"Yes, sah," she whispered sadly.

"Bring me the broth."

She brought it trembling. She was very tired and very hungry, and she wanted to whistle but she only whispered:

"Ain't there nothing I kin do for you?"

"Open the window."

"It's night air, sah—"

"Open it, fool—"

She went to the window and opened it. She was handsome when she reached up, and her nose was almost as excellent as certain Jewish noses; her throat was smooth, and it throbbed.

Toward ten o'clock that night John Hardaway began to sing to himself. He was fond of French, but what he learned in French he sang in English.

"Ah, my little one—I have held you on my knee—

"I have kissed your ears and throat—

"Now I set you down—

"You may do as you will."

He tried to turn over—but failed, and so he lay there staring into the fire.

At this point in the death of John Hardaway, Rabb, the nigger, came out of her corner, and ceased trembling. She was hungry and began heating some soup in a saucepan.

"What are you doing?" John Hardaway inquired abruptly.

"I's hungry, sah."

"Then get out of here—get into the kitchen."

"Yes, sah," but she did not move.

John Hardaway breathed heavily, a mist went over his eyes—presently, after interminable years, he lifted his lids. Rabb was now slowly sipping the steaming soup.

"You damned nigger!"

She got up from her haunches hurriedly—placing her hand in front of her, backing toward the door.

"Little one, I have taken you on my knee—"

Rabb crept back—she came up to the bed.

"Massah, don't you think—?"

"What?"

"A priest—maybe?"

"Fool!"

"Yes, sah, I only wanted to make safe."

He tried to laugh. He pressed his knees together. He had forgotten her.

Finally toward dawn he began to wander.

Rabb moistened the roll of red flesh inside her lip and set her teeth. She began to grin at nothing at all, stroking her hips.

He called to her.

"I want to tell you something."

She came forward—rolling her eyes.

"Come closer."

She came.

"Lean down!" She leaned down, but already the saliva began to fill her mouth.

"Are you frightened?"

"No, sah," she lied.

He raised his hand but it fell back, feebly. "Keep your place," he whispered, and instantly went to sleep.

He began to rattle in his throat, while Rabb crouched in the corner, holding her breasts in her folded arms and rocking softly on the balls of her feet.

The rattling kept on. Rabb began creeping toward him on hands and knees.

"Massah!"

He did not move.

"John!"

He felt a strange sensation—he lifted his eyelids with their fringe of white lashes and almost inaudibly said:

"Now go!"

He had closed his eyes a long time, when he was troubled with the thought that someone was trying to get into his body as he left it. He opened his eyes and there stood Rabb the nigger very close, looking down at him.

A gush of blood sprang from his nose.

"No, sah!"

He began to gasp. Rabb the nigger stood up to her full height and looked down at him. She began to fan him, quickly. He breathed more hurriedly, his chest falling together like a house of cards. He tried to speak, he could not.

Suddenly Rabb bent down and leaning her mouth to his, breathed into him, one great and powerful breath. His chest rose, he opened his eyes, said "Ah!" and died.

Rabb ran her tongue along her lips, and raising her eyes, stared at a spot on the wall a little higher than she was wont to. After a while she remembered her unfinished soup.

LULLABY

———

When I was a young child I slept with a dog,
I lived without trouble and I thought no harm;
I ran with the boys and I played leap-frog;
Now it is a girl's head that lies on my arm.

Then I grew a little, picked plantain in the yard;
Now I dwell in Greenwich, and the people do not call;
Then I planted pepper-seed and stamped on them hard.
Now I am very quiet and I hardly plan at all.

Then I pricked my finger on a thorn, or a thistle,
Put the finger in my mouth, and ran to my mother.
Now I lie here, with my eyes on a pistol.
There will be a morrow, and another, and another.

INDIAN SUMMER

———

At the age of fifty-three Madame Boliver was young again. She was suddenly swept away in a mad current of reckless and beautiful youth. What she had done with those years that had counted up into such a perfect conclusion, she could not tell—it was a strange, vague dream. She had been plain, almost ugly, shy, an old maid. She was tall and awkward—she sat down as if she were going to break when she was in those new years that girls call early bloom.

When she was thirty she had been frankly and astonishingly Yankee; she came toward one with an erect and angular stride. She was severe, silent and curious. It was probably due to this that she was called Madame. She dressed in black outlined with white collar and cuffs, her hair was drawn straight back and showed large lobed and pale ears. The tight drawn hair exposed her features to that utter and unlovely nakedness that some clean rooms are exposed to by the catching back of heavy and melancholy curtains—she looked out upon life with that same unaccustomed and expectant expression that best rooms wear when thrown open for the one yearly festivity that proclaims their owners well to do.

She had no friends and could not keep acquaintances—her speech was sharp, quick and truthful. She spoke seldom, but with such fierce strictness and accuracy that those who came into contact with her once, took precautions not to be thus exposed a second time.

She grew older steadily and without regret—long before the age of thirty she had given up all expectations of a usual life or any hopes of that called "unusual"; she walked in a straight path between the two, and she was content and speculated little upon this thing in her that had made her unloved and unlovely.

Her sisters had married and fallen away about her as blossoms are carried off, leaving the stalk—their children came like bits of pollen and she enjoyed them and was mildly happy. Once she, too, had dreamed of love, but that was before she had attained to the age of seventeen—by that time she knew that no one could or would ask for her hand—she was plain and unattractive and she was satisfied.

She had become at once the drudge and the adviser—all things were laid upon her both to solve and to produce. She laboured for others easily and willingly and they let her labour.

At fifty-three she blazed into a riotous Indian Summer of loveliness. She was tall and magnificent. She carried with her a flavour of some exotic flower; she exhaled something that savoured of those excellences of odour and tone akin to pain and to pleasure; she lent a plastic embodiment to all hitherto unembodied things. She was like some rare wood, carved into a melting form—she breathed abruptly as one who has been dead for half a century.

Her face, it is true, was not that plump, downy and senseless countenance of the early young—it was thin and dark and marked with a few very sensitive wrinkles; about the mouth there were signs of a humour she had never possessed, of a love she had never known, of a joy she had never experienced and of a wisdom impossible for her to have acquired. Her still, curious eyes with their blue-white borders and the splendid irises were half veiled by strange dusty lids. The hair, that had once been drawn back, was still drawn back, but no appallingly severe features were laid bare. Instead the hair seemed to confer a favour on all those who might look upon its restrained luxury, for it uncovered a face at once valuable and unusual.

Her smile was rich in colour—the scarlet of her gums, the strange whiteness of her teeth, the moisture of the sensitive mouth, all seemed as if Madame Boliver were something dyed through with perfect and rare life.

Now when she entered a room everyone paused, looking up and speaking together. She was quite conscious of this and it pleased her—not because she was too unutterably vain, but because it was so new and so unexpected.

For a while her very youth satisfied her—she lived with herself as though she were a second person who had been permitted access to the presence of some lovely and some longed-for dream.

She did not know what to do. If she could have found religion newly with her new youth she would have worshipped and have been profoundly glad of the kneeling down and the rising up attendant with faith, but this was a part of her old childhood and it did not serve.

She had prayed then because she was ugly; she could not pray now because she was beautiful—she wanted something new to stand before, to speak to.

One by one the old and awkward things went, leaving in their wake Venetian glass and bowls of onyx, silks, cushions and perfume. Her books became magazines with quaint, unsurpassable and daring illustrations.

Presently she had a salon. She was the rage. Gentlemen in political whiskers, pomaded and curled, left their coats in the embrace of pompous and refined footmen.

Young students with boutonnières and ambitions came; an emissary or two dropped in, proffered their hearts and departed. Poets and musicians, littérateurs and artists experimenting in the modern, grouped themselves about her mantels like butterflies over bonbons and poured sentiment upon sentiment into her ears.

Several gentlemen of leisure and millions courted her furiously with small tears in the corners of their alert eyes. Middle-aged professors and one deacon were among the crowd that filled her handsome apartment on those days when she entertained.

There was something about Madame Boliver that could not quite succumb to herself. She was still afraid; she would start, draw her hand away and pale abruptly in the middle of some ardent proposal—she would hurry to the mirror at such times, though she never turned her head to look in.

Was it possible that she was beautiful now? And if so, would it remain? And her heart said, "Yes, it will remain," until at last she believed it.

She put the past behind her and tried to forget it. It hurt her to remember it, as if it were something that she had done in a moment of absent-mindedness and of which she had to be ashamed. She remembered it as one remembers some small wrong deed hidden for years. She thought about her past unattractiveness as another would have thought of some cruelty. Her eyes watered when she remembered her way of looking at herself in her twenties. Her mouth trembled when she thought back to its severity and its sharp retorts.

Her very body reproached her for all that had been forced upon it in her other youth, and a strange passion came upon her, turning her memory of her sisters into something at times like that hatred felt by the oppressed who remember the oppression when it has given way to plenty.

But now she was free. She expanded, she sang, she dreamed for long hours, her elbows upon the casement, looking out into the garden. She smiled, remembering the old custom of serenading, and wondered when she, too, would know it.

That she was fifty-three never troubled her. It never even occurred to her. She had been fifty-three long ago at twenty, and now she was twenty at fifty-three, that was all—this was compensation, and if she had been through her middle age in youth she could go through her youth in middle age.

At times she thought how much more beautiful nature is in its treacheries than its remedies.

Those who hovered about her offered, time on time, to marry her, to carry her away into Italy or to Spain, to lavish money and devotion on her, and in the beginning she had been almost too ready to accept them in their assurances, because the very assurances were so new and so delightful.

But in spite of it she was, somewhere beneath her youth, old enough to know that she did not love as she would love, and she waited with a patience made pleasant by the constant attentions of the multitude.

And then Petkoff, "the Russian," had come, accompanied by one of the younger students.

A heavy fur cap came down to the borders of his squinting and piercing eyes. He wore a mixture of clothing that proclaimed him at once foreign and poor. His small moustache barely covered sensitive and well shaped lips, and the little line of hair that reached down on each side of his close-set ears gave him an early period expression as if he, too, in spite of his few years, might have lived in the time when she was a girl.

He could not have been much over thirty, perhaps just thirty— he said little but never took his eyes off the object of his interest.

He spoke well enough, with an occasional lapse into Russian, which was very piquant. He swept aside all other aspirants with his steady and centred gaze. He ignored the rest of the company so completely as to rob him of rudeness. If one is ignorant of the very presence of his fellow beings, at most he can only be called "strange."

Petkoff was both an ambitious and a self-centred man—all his qualities were decisive and not hesitatingly crooked, providing he needed crookedness to win his point. He was attractive to Madame Boliver because he was as strange as she was herself, her youth was foreign, and so was Petkoff.

He had come to this country to start a venture that promised to be successful; in the meantime, he had to be careful both in person and in heart.

What he felt for Madame Boliver was at first astonishment that such a woman was still unmarried; he knew nothing of her past, and guessed at her age much below the real figure. After a while this astonishment gave way to pleasure and then to real and very sincere love.

He began to pay court to her, neglecting his business a little and worrying over that end of it, but persisting, nevertheless.

He could see that she, on her side, was becoming deeply attached to him. He would walk about in the park for hours arguing this affair out to himself. Both the shoulds and should nots.

It got him nowhere except into a state of impatience. He liked clear-cut acts and he could not decide to go or stay. As it was, nothing could be worse for his business than this same feverish indecision. He made up his mind.

Madame Boliver was radiantly happy. She began to draw away from a life of entertainment and, instead, turned most of her energies into the adoration of her first real love. She accepted him promptly, and with a touch of her old firm and sharp decisiveness, and a hint of her utter frankness. He told her that she took him as she would have taken a piece of cake at a tea party, and they both laughed.

That was in the Winter. Madame Boliver was fifty-five—he never asked her how old she was and she never thought to tell him. They set the day for their wedding early in the following June.

They were profoundly happy. One by one the younger, more ardent admirers fell off, but very slowly; they turned their heads a little as they went, being both too vain and too skeptical to believe that this would last.

She still held receptions and still her rooms were flooded, but when Petkoff entered, a little better dressed but still a bit heedless of the throng, they hushed their highest hilarities and spoke of the new novels and the newest trend in art.

Petkoff had taken notice of them to that degree necessary to a man who knows what he has won, and from whom and how many. He looked upon them casually, but with a hint of well-being.

Madame Boliver grew more beautiful, more radiant, more easeful. Her movements began to resemble flowing water; she was almost too happy, too supple, too conscious of her well-being. She became arrogant, but still splendid; she became vain, but still gracious; she became accustomed to herself, but still reflective. She could be said to have bloomed at too auspicious an age; she was old enough to appreciate it, and this is a very dangerous thing.

She spent hours at the hair dresser's and the dressmaker's. Her dressing table resembled a battlefield. It supported all the armament for keeping age at a distance. She rode in the avenue in an open carriage, and smiled when the society notices mentioned her name and ran her picture.

She finally gave one the impression of being beautiful, but too conscious of it; talented, but too vain; easy of carriage, but too reliant on it; of being strange and rare and wonderful, but a little too strange, a little too rare, a little too wonderful. She became magnificently complex to outward appearances, yet in her soul Madame Boliver still kept her honesty, her frankness and her simplicity.

And then one day Madame Boliver took to her bed. It began with a headache and ended with severe chills. She hoped to get up on the following day, and she remained there a week; she put her party off, expecting to be able to be about, but instead she gave it sitting in a chair supported by cushions.

Petkoff was worried and morose. He had given a good deal of time to Madame Boliver, and he cared for her in a selfish and all-engrossing way. When she stood up no longer he broke a Venetian tumbler by throwing it into the fireplace. When she laughed at this he suddenly burst out into very heavy weeping. She tried to comfort him, but he would not be comforted. She promised him that she would walk soon, as a mother promises a child some longed-for object. When she said, "I will be well, dear, soon; after all I'm a young woman," he stopped and looked at her through a film of painful tears.

"But are you?" he said, voicing for the first time his inner fear.

And it was then that the horror of the situation dawned upon her. In youth, when youth comes rightly, there is old age in which to lose it complacently, but when it comes in old age there is no time to watch it go.

She sat up and stared at him.

"Why, yes," she said in a flat and firm voice, "that's so. I am no longer of few years."

She could not say "no longer young," because she was young.

"It will make no difference."

"Ah," she said, "it will make no difference to you, but it will make a difference to us."

She lay back and sighed, and presently she asked him to leave her a little while.

When he had gone she summoned the doctor.

She said: "My friend—am I dying—so soon?"

He shook his head emphatically. "Of course not," he assured her; "we will have you up in a week or so."

"What is it, then, that keeps me here now?"

"You have tired yourself out, that is all. You see, such extensive entertaining, my dear madame, will tax the youngest of us." He shook his head at this and twisted his moustache. She sent him away also.

The next few days were happy ones. She felt better. She sat up without fatigue. She was joyful in Petkoff's renewed affections. He had been frightened, and he lavished more extravagant praise and endearing terms on her than ever before. He was like a man who, seeing his fortune go, found how dear it was to him after all and how necessary when it returned to him. By almost losing her he appreciated what he should have felt if he had lost her indeed.

It got to be a joke between them that they had held any fears at all. At the club he beat his friends on the back and cried:

"Gentlemen, a beautiful and young woman." And they used to beat his back, exclaiming: "Lucky, by God!"

She ordered a large stock of wine and cakes for the wedding party, bought some new Venetian glasses and indulged in a few rare old carpets for the floor. She had quite a fancy, too, for a new gown offered at a remarkably low sum, but she began to curb herself, for she had been very extravagant as it was.

And then one day she died.

Petkoff came in a wild, strange mood. Four candles were burning at head and feet, and Madame Boliver was more lovely than ever. Stamping, so that he sent up little spirals of dust from the newly acquired carpet, Petkoff strode up and down beside the bier. He leaned over and lit a cigarette by one of the flickering flames of the candles. Madame Boliver's elderly sister, who was kneeling, coughed and looked reproachfully upward at the figure of Petkoff, who had once again forgotten everyone and everything. "Damn it!" he said, putting his fingers into his vest.

I'D HAVE YOU THINK OF ME

———

As one who, leaning on the wall, once drew
Thick blossoms down, and hearkened to the hum
Of heavy bees slow rounding the wet plum,
And heard across the fields the patient coo
Of restless birds bewildered with the dew.

As one whose thoughts were mad in painful May,
With melancholy eyes turned toward her love,
And toward the troubled earth whereunder throve
The chilly rye and coming hawthorn spray—
With one lean, pacing hound, for company.

THE RABBIT

———

The road was covered with red and yellow leaves. Rugo Amietieve, who said that he was an Armenian, had wished one of those lingering good-byes to this rotund and plentiful day that only a man of slow and methodical mind can bring into being. He bid it adieu with more than the silence and the love of his heart; he had whispered over it, his square yellow teeth a little apart and touching the moist curve of his under-lip with the small round point of flesh that clung to his upper like a tear. He said good-bye resolutely and quite peacefully, with the restraint of a man who knows what's bad for him and why. Rugo did not want to leave the country, but he had to. He knew why he did not want to, and he knew why he was being forced to—necessity—that was it, necessity had been hurrying his people about the world from the beginning of time and would hurry them.

Farewell held no piquancy for him, he did not tear out his heart by his departure; there was nothing in the fact of the sunlight and the blowing and dying leaves that gave him sweet pain and too heavy sorrow; the red of the fallen apples sent no pang into the very midst of his being. On the contrary Rugo Amietieve felt only that sense of loss that a good housewife feels when she is letting a rich quilt out of her fingers. In the soil, as Rugo had known it, had been life, hard and fragrant. He had toiled at the plough grumbling, but sensing, with a slow, precise pleasure, that the air was warm and good and healthy. He had tended his geese and his cows with the same stolid satisfaction, and he watched them moving about, leaning on his two folded and brown hands. The ducks' yellow, gaping mouths gave him physical pleasure, he would have liked to press his hand over them where they were all shining and brittle; it would have given him as much pleasure as a flower petal—more, because these living things that cackled and spread their wings and brought forth young were profitable also—the world lived here and moved, and its incidental placing of him where he could profit by it was the thing that amazed and satisfied him.

Now it was otherwise. He must go away into the city where, they said, nothing was fresh and new and living. His uncle had died, leaving him his little tailoring establishment on the East Side. There Rugo was bound, there from this day forward he would sit and sew interminably as though he were a machine—as though he had suddenly died and had to work.

He lifted his straight nose and smelled the September air. Here the woods dipped over the road, spilling shadows gigantic and restless, with a speckling of ragged sun patches like flowers. Mosquitoes came up from the swamp as the night descended and sang about Rugo's ears and set him swearing. They got into the long, tangled meshes of his beard and clung there; they sat in among these thick, ruddy strands and hissed against the shuddering flesh of his cheeks. He lifted one of his hands and struck his face on either side, and went on.

The next morning the East Side, in the early Thirties, saw a stranger sweeping out what had been old Amietieve's shop. Rugo looked about him with sad eyes. The room was twelve feet by twenty-four and the back part was curtained off by a hanging of dull green, sprinkled over with pink roses; a small cot bed was thus hidden from the front of the shop. It was within these four walls that Rugo must live. He turned around in it, sniffing the air with his long nose, laid back again as he had done in the last hour in the country. He sneered. "You're a little fool room," he said, "to be so small." It was as if he were shaking it, as a child is shaken and held up to learn by another's larger and more important example. He held this room up by the scruff of its neck and shook it in the face of the thirty acres he had known, and he sneered upon it.

He had learned the trade when still a child, when this same uncle had been guardian, but his fingers were freedom clumsy and he broke the needle.

Work came hesitatingly and painfully. Rugo was a slow man, and at this task he was still more laborious and backward. He toiled far into the night seated upon his table, his goose between his knees. People walking by on their way home sometimes peered in over the top of the cardboard sign specked by the flies and the open fashion book with its strange, angular, shiny gentlemen carrying canes and looking over their shoulders playfully as if they were keeping something very amusing in their minds to hand out like favours; and such people often said, "That chap will die of consumption, you see."

The butcher's shop across the way seemed to be vying with the remnants of silks and serge in Rugo's window. There were rump ends and flanks and knuckle bones, remnants of some fine animal, all wonderful and red and satiny yellow where the layers of fat crept out like frostings, or where fat spread over kidneys like irregular lace; yet to Rugo they were somehow painful, they made him think of the cows and the poultry that he had so often gazed fondly upon, of the animal life he had grown up among, and he turned his head away and went on stitching.

Rugo got his own breakfast, lunch, dinner. Behind the curtain there, beside his bed, was a small gas stove. In the Winter the shop was deadly with heavy air. He could not open the door or he would have flooded the place in a moment with cold, piercing and cruel, so he sat in the foul air of a gas burner, and his eyes grew so dark in the paling face that the children of the neighbourhood called him "Coal Eye."

In the Summer business had picked up, though Rugo seldom had any time to himself. He worked quicker, but then orders were more plentiful on patches, turnings and pressings. He had become attached to a small, ill and very slender Italian girl who came once with her father's coat.

Her straight parted dark hair made him think of animals, he thought her gentle and Madonna-like, not taking into account a small, cruel and avaricious mouth. It was very red and he was pleased with it. Almost anything bright pleased him. The very fact that these lips were cruel pleased him, though he did not know that it was the brightness of calculation that made them attractive to him.

Rugo was not a good-looking man, but this did not trouble him; he was as good-looking as anyone he had ever seen, and therefore he was unconscious that for so large a head, his body was rather small.

This girl Addie told him. It hurt him, because he was beginning to like her. He noticed that when his lip trembled her eyes got very bright. "Why," he asked her, puzzled, "do you always look so pretty when you say things like that?"

This flattered her, but it only made it worse for Rugo. She was indeed a very common woman, with a little to make her young and pretty, and she made the most of it.

Finally he spoke to her quietly and slowly about love and marriage. Of course Addie, in her shrewd mind, had calculated on this; his was a business that threatened to prosper, and she was attracted to him, anyway. She made her plans accordingly; she acted displeased.

"You are a poor, common tradesman," she said bitterly, as if she were something uncommon and therefore beyond him. He felt this, too, and instead of discovering her own smallness in the retort, he only got the point she wanted him to get. He began to think himself below her. He raised his hand:

"What do you want that I shall do?"

She shrugged her narrow shoulders and laughed, showing a red tongue that seemed to crouch in her mouth in a long, dented line.

"But I must do something, you say I am only—"

"You shall never be anything else."

"True, but I may be more."

"Hardly."

"Why do you say 'hardly'?"

"You are not the sort of person—now, for instance—"

"Yes?" he questioned slowly, turning around and looking into her face.

"Well, for instance, you are hardly a hero."

"Are heroes the style?" he asked pitifully. This made her laugh even harder.

"Not in your family, I take it."

He nodded. "Yes, that's true—we were always quiet people. You do not like quiet people?"

"They are like women," she answered.

He pondered awhile over this. He shook his head; after all he knew better and he was angry because he had been letting Addie lie to him.

"That is not true."

She began to scream at him:

"So, that's the way you begin, calling me a liar, is it?" She put her hands into her hair on either side and tore at it. This had even more of an effect upon Rugo than she had expected. He beat his hands together. In spoiling the perfect oval of her head, in ruinously shaking its smooth and parted hair, she had hurt him as much as if she had shaken a holy picture.

"No, no," he cried. "I will do something, you shall see—it is all right—it is all right." He approached her and, touching her shoulder with his hand, he added:

"For you I will do it—I will do it."

She smiled. "You will do what, Rugo Amietieve?"

"I shall be less like a woman. You called me like a woman; well, you shall see."

She came close to him, her two thin arms pressed close to her side.

"You will do something big and grand—Rugo—for me?"

He looked down at her, puzzled and quiet. The cruel mouth was half open, showing the shining line of her teeth. He nodded, but this time he moved away from her and stood staring out into the street.

She came up behind him, caught both of his hands, and, leaning forward, kissed him on the back of his neck. He tried to turn,
but she held his two hands a moment longer and then broke out of
the shop at a run.

Presently he set to work again, sitting cross-legged on his table.

He wondered what he was expected to do. He had often spoken to her of returning to the country, with a hint in his voice that
she would be there beside him, too. Now it had come to this.

He pondered. A hero—what was a hero—what made the difference between a hero and himself, anyway? He remembered tales
the gypsies had told him about their greatest men when he had
been in the old land of his birth. They told a story of a lad who
fought and fought, and finding himself unequal to the task of killing his rival, flung himself off a mountain.

What would be the use of that—he would die, and then he
might as well not have lived. He thought of all the great people
he had read of, or had heard of, or had known. There was Jean the
blacksmith, who had lost an eye saving his child from a horse. If he
lost an eye Addie would not like him.

Napoleon—there was a well-known man; he had done so many
things, it seemed, for which people framed him in white enamel
and hung him upon their bedroom walls; but chiefly he had been
renowned for his killing. Rugo thought about that awhile and
came to the illuminating conclusion that all heroes were men who
killed or were killed.

Well, the last was impossible; if he was killed he might just as
well have starved in the country and not have laid eyes on Addie.
Therefore, he must kill—but what—but whom?

Of course, he might save something or somebody, but they
would have to be in danger first, and there might not be any danger for days and days, and he was tired of waiting.

Presently he laid his work aside, lowered the shade, and, lying
face down on his bed, he tried to think it all out clearly.

Presently he got a vivid picture of killing in his mind. He sat
up and put his hands two or three times over his face. It was damp.
He sat on the edge of the bed and looked at the carpet. His mind

wandered. He thought of the ducks he had longed to stroke, of the gentle, feeding cows, of the fresh, clean air—then he thought again of Addie and of what he must do. He tried to picture himself killing someone. He put his two hands together and looked at them—there, that was the way. Then he smiled. His hands, set as they were, could not have choked anything larger than a thrush. He widened them, but he separated them instantly and rubbed them down his legs, breathing heavily. What a terrible business a hero's was! He thought of the throbbing that must stop beneath such hands as his. He got up, shaking his shoulders from side to side as if his back hurt him. He pulled up the shade.

The butcher's windows opposite attracted his attention. Two gas lights were burning there vividly. Rugo could see flanks of beef laid out in pans, little ruddy pools collecting about them like insertion. Fowl hung by the necks and several hams lured the passer-by as they swung softly this way and that.

He opened his door hesitatingly and shutting it carefully stepped out into the roadway.

He crossed over and leaned his head against the glass. He looked in very close now, and he could see the film that shrouded the dead eyes of the fowl and the hares. Slabs of liver laid out in heaps, flanked by cuts of tripe, drew his attention.

A strange sensation had hold of him in the pit of his stomach. It seemed to him that he was turning pale. He raised his hand to his beard and tugged at it.

Two or three red hairs separated and came out. He held them up between him and the light. Then he darted in the back door of the shop.

Presently he emerged carrying a box. With the furtive and hurried step of a man who is being observed he crossed the street. He opened the door of his own little shop and, locking it quickly, he put the box in the corner and turned down the light.

It was very dark and he stumbled. A little reflection came from the meat shop window and touched the rims of his cardboards, and his pattern book full of the funny strutting gentlemen. His heart was beating horribly against his side. He began to question himself and stopped. He could never do it unless he made his mind a resolute thing. He clenched his teeth, blinking his eyes as he did so. He began to shiver.

Presently he threw himself on the ground in the corner near the box, his arms over his head, his face flat upon the dust and grime of the boards. He must do it quickly—but he couldn't do it.

His mind began to wander again. He thought of the road, red and yellow with the dying leaves of Autumn, of the great swaying shadows and the sunlight breaking in between in little jagged spots like flowers. He remembered the mosquitoes, and he got to his knees and let his hands hang down at his sides.

The Summer had always been so pretty; the rains left the fields so bright and sudden when they came into view over the top of the hill. The ploughing had been good, he had really enjoyed that after all, only then he had not known just how much he did enjoy it. What a pity that he had not known what a good thing it all was then.

Something moved beside him, breathing softly. He uttered a sharp cry and the same thing moved back, hitting a board, and was again silent.

He bent forward, thrust his two hands out, closed them— tighter, tighter and tighter. A faint cry, a little jerking to and fro— that was all.

He stood up and turned the light on. He looked at his hands. Then backing away from the corner, never letting his eyes rest there, he plunged his hands up to the elbows in a pail of water. He threw a cupful of it inside his shirt at the neck. He opened the door. Addie was there.

She came in softly, gently, insinuatingly. She could see by his face that something very horrible and necessary had been done. She saw by his face how it had hurt, by his hands what it must have cost him.

She came close to him. "What have you done, Rugo?" she said.

"I—I have killed," he said, almost in a whisper.

"What—where?" She moved toward the centre of the room and then looked into the corner.

"That?" she began to laugh.

"Take it or leave it," he said suddenly in a loud and penetrating voice.

She stooped and lifted it up—a small grey rabbit.

She laid it down again. She placed her arm about him.

"Come quickly," she said. "Comb your hair."

She pushed him into the street. She was afraid of him, for there was something strange and hard in his mouth and he walked putting each foot down very flat and steady.

"Where are you going? What are you going to do?" He did not seem to know that she was there, clinging to him, her arm about his waist. He had forgotten her. He looked up into the air, sniffing it and smiling.

"Come," she said, "we are going to have your boots shined."

THE FLOWERING CORPSE

So still she lies in this closed place apart,
Her feet grown fragile for the ghostly tryst;
Her pulse no longer striking in her wrist,
Nor does its echo wander through her heart.

Over the body and the quiet head
Like stately ferns above an austere tomb,
Soft hairs blow; and beneath her armpits bloom
The drowsy passion flowers of the dead.

A BOY ASKS A QUESTION OF A LADY

———

The days had been very warm and quick. It was Fall now and everything was drawing to a close. It had been a bad, but somehow pleasant, year. A great number of people had been disillusioned and were not seen hurrying from one place to another, as is customary with those of undisturbed habit. They went slowly, and it was said that Winter with its snow and frost would be most welcome.

Carmen la Tosca was in the habit of riding at a swift gallop down the lane and into the copse beyond. She leaned ever so little in her saddle as she went under the boughs. The plume of her hat bent and swung smartly back into place as she rounded the curve.

Her horse was a clear cascade of white. The shining forelock, the soft descending plane of the frontal bone melted into a taut nostril. And where Carmen la Tosca broke the living line of its back with her own, the spine flowed beneath her as deftly as water, and quivered into massive alert haunches, which in turn socketed in velvet, a foaming length of tail.

Carmen la Tosca rode well. She let more than usual of her pelvis drop into the saddle. Upon the reins she kept gloved hands in a grip that was consciously lacking in direction.

Carmen la Tosca was an actress. She had played in "Fife and Fiddle" and "Drums of the King."

She took parts suggesting a love of danger and intrigue. She was always handsomely gloved and shod, and her dresses were widely copied.

She had been in stock, and in the beginning had sung in opera; she had been the Queen in "Aïda" and she had played a boy's part in vaudeville. Now she was resting.

She was not the kind of woman who usually came to this quiet country town, snuggled, as they say, among the foothills. The boy who kept the general store said she was "stunning." Little children ran backward ahead of her, crying provokingly, "Red lips, red lips!" But no one really knew her.

She had appeared in the Spring of the year with a man-servant and a maid. For two days she had been seen at the windows hanging curtains. When they were all hung no one saw her for some time. Then she bought a white horse and rode it. And after that she always rode on the white horse, though she had six or seven others before the Fall came. Usually she rode alone. Now and again a gentleman, with a birth-mark twisting his face into an unwilling irony, rode beside her. There was a goat path in the underbrush and here two boys sometimes came and lay and talked of her and waited for her to pass, riding that smart way on the white mare. These boys were Brandt and Bailey Wilson, a farmer's sons. Sometimes couples, going berrying by the mountain road, came near enough to hear her laughing behind the casement.

Sometimes she walked, descending the hill carefully, avoiding the melon plants, talking brightly to a young man, but paying little attention to the effect of her words, not through vanity, but simply through lack of interest in the effect itself.

There was a great deal of gossip about her of course. She did not court mystery, but it was all about her.

People said that she was not exactly beautiful, neither was she ugly. Her face held the elements of both in perfect control. She was brutally chic.

A lean, tall woman of the village, who had come from London, said Carmen la Tosca's back was like the Queen's. This was probably an exaggeration.

Carmen la Tosca breakfasted in bed and late. She dusted her arms with talc and she languidly settled into a light lace peignoir. She had tea and rolls, and the bed stood between two unvarnished cherry-wood ovals, in which were imprisoned two engravings of officials of the Tower of London, in its bloodiest hour.

The double windows faced the orchard. She turned her back to the orchard and its falling apples, and read St. Francis, or the morning paper which was, by the time she received it, a day or two old.

The room was bare and grey and rustic. And in this Carmen la Tosca and her bed made a strange contrast. She liked to think of it unless she had other things on her mind. If the morning was chilly she had a quilted jacket, and if it was raining she had the shades raised that she might watch the rain falling a long way.

Early in the morning the boy chose it had been raining, but about eleven it had stopped and the sun was trying to come out. Carmen la Tosca could smell how wet everything was.

The boy was Brandt Wilson, fourteen; he had done rather well at the high school of the nearest large town. He was short and his head was large and his face already a little prematurely softened by melancholy. He was splashed with mud and his red tie stuck out ridiculously at the top of a vest that was too large for his small, shyly muscular chest.

He stood before her on the rug, his hat in his hand.

Carmen la Tosca, with a single movement, rolled over in bed.

"Who are you? Where did you come from?"

"I am Brandt Wilson. I came through the window. It was very easy."

"Well," she said. "What is it?"

The child hesitated, and with a look of distress, managed to say:

"I have a brother."

Carmen la Tosca pushed away the paper and regarded him with amusement, and a little amazement.

"He is two years older than I am—and there's something I don't understand—and you know everything."

"Who said so?"

"The neighbours, my father, my mother, my sister, the school-master, the postman—"

"That will do."

"You are a woman of the world." The childish sound of his voice became terribly apparent.

"My brother is where no one understands—My sister said, 'I don't like Bailey any more, he has lost that cunning little light in his eyes'—and I said, 'It's still there when you give him something he likes, and he is untying it, with his head bent down—'"

"How do you come to think of all this?"

"Once the sun was shining and we had been lying out on the bank with our arms under our heads and then he said—he confessed"—the child faltered, then looking at her directly and fixedly, said, "Bailey cried when he knew it was over—"

"What was over?"

"I asked him, and he answered, 'I am a man now.' Shall I cry, too, when I know that? What is it all about?"

Carmen la Tosca rose on her elbow and looked at him with suffused eyes as if she had been crying, but it was all an illusion.

"How many of you are there?"

"Three. A married brother."

"And how old is he?"

"Twenty-four. He cried once, too, but differently, about his sweetheart. She died, you know, and when they told him he said, crying out, 'I could have saved her.' We asked him how, but he would not tell us, but he told mother; he said, 'I would have said I love you.' Is there such a power?"

Carmen la Tosca lay on her back, her hands beside her.

"That was innocence. We are all waiting for the day when people shall learn of our innocence, all over again," she said brightly.

"And is that suffering?"

"Yes, a special kind, for everyone," she said gravely. "But not a personal torment. You are not to believe in that. Suffering is all alike, yours, mine, everybody's. All these distinctions and what people say about them is nonsense. Suffering is all the same everywhere for everyone." She suddenly rose up in bed and said, softly, "Now you do not want to talk to me any more?"

He moved his fingers on the foot-board of the bed.

"I'm sorry," she said hastily, covered with confusion. "It's my indolence that does it."

"What?" he asked timidly.

"Embarrasses you."

"It's all right."

"Now see here," she continued. "Do you ever think of animals?"

"Why?"

"Do you?"

"I don't know. I notice them—"

"Capital!" she cried, clapping her hands; "that's what I wanted to know. Well then, what would all this, you and I and your great trouble, mean to them?"

"I don't know what you mean."

"Your questions, my answers? Nothing."

He coloured, and looked down. "What does it mean?" he repeated, and as he said it he could not remember what he had come for, or what he had said, and while she was answering he tried desperately to re-establish himself.

He said, "And you do not know what I must go through before I feel like Bailey?"

"A little evil day by day, that makes everything grow."

"Yes, that is what I wanted to know," he said, breathlessly.

"Listen then, it's all that makes the difference between a gentleman and a fool. Never do evil to good people, they always forgive it, and that is nasty."

"But what about all these things that people talk of and I do not understand?"

"The simple story, simply told by simple people—that in the end is all you will listen to."

"And I'm not to try to make anything out of all this?"

"No," she said, "nothing at all, leave it alone."

"And not to try to understand what made him cry?"

"Just as it is. The calf is born, she lies in the sun; she waits for the end. That is dignity."

"But sometimes I'm unhappy."

"In the end you will know you know nothing. That will be the death of you."

Brandt stood still, though she had taken up her paper.

"Just that?"

"Come here," she said, and he came, quickly. She put her hand out with a gentle laugh and touched him. "There, that's all."

He went away then.

FIRST COMMUNION

———

The mortal fruit upon the bough
Hangs above the nuptial bed.
The cat-bird in the tree returns
The forfeit of his mutual vow.

The hard, untimely apple of
The branch that feeds on watered rain
Takes the place upon her lips
Of her late lamented love.

Many hands together press
Shaped within a static prayer
Recall to one the chorister
Docile in his sexless dress.

The temperate winds reclaim the iced
Remorseless vapours of the snow.
The only pattern in the mind
Is the cross behind the Christ.

FINIS

———

For you, for me? Why then the striking hour,
The wind among the curtains, and the tread
Of some late gardener pulling at the flower
They'll lay between our hearts when we are dead.

Torin McLachlan is a PhD Candidate in English Language & Literatures at the University of British Columbia. His dissertation in progress focuses on the appropriation of "exhaustion" – as both an experience and a style – in modernist writing and more contemporary humanities scholarship. He currently teaches at Capilano University, living and working on the unceded territories of the Líỉwat, xʷməθkʷəy̓əm (Musqueam), shíshálh (Sechelt), Skwxwú7mesh (Squamish) and Səl̓ílwəta?/Selilwitulh (Tsleil-Waututh) Nations.

Milton Keynes UK
Ingram Content Group UK Ltd.
UKHW010642271123
433342UK00003B/45